MILITARY TECHNOLOGY

Exeter Books

NEW YORK

Editor: Mark Dartford
Art Editor: Eddie Pitcher

First published in USA 1985
by Exeter Books
Distributed by Bookthrift
Exeter is a trademark of Simon & Schuster, Inc.
Bookthrift is a registered trademark of Simon & Schuster
New York, New York

ISBN 0-671-07575-6

Printed in Italy

Endpapers **The highly maneouverable Scimitar armoured reconnaissance vehicle is put through its paces during a battle exercise.**

Right **First vertical-launch test firing of Seawolf anti-missile missile. The advantage of vertical launch is to reduce cramping and increase payload on crowded ship decks.**

Overleaf **The US Pershing 2 tactical nuclear missile.**

INTRODUCTION

Military Technology offers a fascinating glimpse into the future world of warfare. The science of warfare has always exemplified the pinnacle of human ingenuity – yet very often for uses that ultimately serve the cause of peace better than war.

In the air, *Military Technology* looks at machines that defy all the known laws of aerodynamics – by flying backwards or 'jumping' to avoid enemy missiles. One such aircraft is hardly an aircraft at all – a more accurate description might be 'flying gun'! In space, the satellite race has already begun, with laser and particle beam weapons no longer the stuff of science fiction. On land, new shells that use chemicals to 'melt' the massive armour of a modern tank and guns made of plastic and light as a feather, bear witness to the pace of scientific achievement. At sea, the deadly world beneath the waves is becoming increasingly cluttered with the silent spies and waiting weaponry of tomorrow's undersea battlefield.

In graphic words and illustrations, *Military Technology* examines some of these remarkable advances in the arsenals of the world's leading powers. Will laser-armed satellites be the guardians of our future peace? Can the arms race go on indefinitely, each side stockpiling ever more weapons of destruction than needed to eradicate an enemy? And does new technology always hold the key to the future, or are there sometimes good reasons for rediscovering old ways of doing things? *Military Technology* takes a look at these questions – and offers some answers as well.

CONTENTS

AIR WAR

Perhaps some of the most challenging developments in the technology of modern warfare have taken place above the ground: vertical takeoff, flying guns, revolutionary design concepts and the quest for dominance on the ultimate battlefield – space

An RAF Harrier GR 3 V/STOL aircraft firing non-guided SNEB rockets at a ground target.

THE GATLING GUN TAKES WING

Firing seventy armour-piercing shells a second, the A-10 is the West's most potent flying machine – and probably the toughest thing on two wings when launched in combat against its special target: the tank

The GAU-8 Gatling gun that fills most of the A-10 Thunderbolt II fuselage is one of the most awesome battlefield weapons ever installed in a tactical aircraft. Press the firing button for a one-second burst, and the first 30 mm shell will pierce a tank 3 km distant before the seventieth has left the plane. Such is the performance of a gun 6m long, with seven rotating barrels and a weight of 900 kg. Around this monstrous weapon is constructed a plane that is ugly, cheap and devastating. Pilots love it.

The A-10 is the first jet ever designed exc-

lusively for the demanding task of supporting ground forces, working in close co-operation with them through ground and air liaison officers. Fighters or bombers previously used in close air support missions have been quite unsuited to the job.

Quite unlike the sophisticated, all-purpose miracles of aviation on which Western air forces have relied in recent years, the A-10 is reassuringly rugged. If one of the two General Electric TF34 GE 100 turbofan engines is shot up, the plane can fly on using the other. Similarly, if one of the two tail fins

is damaged, the pilot can stay airborne on the other. In fact, the aircraft is designed so that all possible vital items are duplicated and interchangeable right and left. All its hydraulic systems and basic electronics can run from either engine, or from an auxiliary power unit in the fuselage. If the hydraulic system is destroyed, the pilot has old-fashioned cables linking his stick to the control surfaces.

As well as having such impressive fail-safe properties, the A-10 is protected in other ways. The pilot is cocooned within a

Right **The first jet designed specific- ally to fight in land battles, the A-10 can carry some 7,000 kg of bombs and missiles as well as 1,350 rounds of ammunition** (*left*).

Left **Ruggedly built, cunningly camouflaged and armed to the teeth, four A-10s present a formidable picture as they fly close together in line-ahead formation on a mission.**

box of thick titanium armour-plating, which is reassuringly impervious to anti-aircraft fire; indeed, it is able to resist all but the heaviest-calibre shells. Other important parts of the plane are also armoured or so designed that should they be hit, the air-craft can still make it safely back to base. In addition, the undercarriage is constructed so that, if necessary, it can land even if it is retracted.

Such a tough, straightforward, easily maintained plane is highly cost effective in an era when defence budgets are out of date almost as soon as they are announced; even though an A-10 costs about £2.5 mill-ion, four could be built for the price of a single F-14 fighter. Also, A-10 ammunition is cheap enough to allow pilots ample live ammunition training at sea ranges in Europe (by contrast, the USAF can afford to fire only 200 live air-to-ground missiles each year).

Slow but deft

An enemy gunner's first sight of the A-10 is likely to be at treetop height as it comes in – firing. In the air, most warplanes can out-pace it, for it flies at subsonic speeds. In fact, the A-10 has a startlingly low maximum speed. When heavily burdened with its full load of weaponry, it can manage only about 556 km/h. Even without a load, it flies at a mere 722 km/h.

Despite its slow speed, however, few planes can match the A-10's phenomenal manoeuvrability. Pursuers are likely to meet it coming back at them – firing. Although at 16.25 m it is as long as a World War II Wel-lington bomber or a small jet airliner, it has a turning circle of only 1,220 m and can out-flank almost any pursuer. Pilots of super-sonic USAF F-14s flying combat training exercises against A-10s were impressed to see their slow but agile 'enemies' bank tightly to meet them head-on.

The story would be no different if the op-ponent were a real one in the shape of a Russian Mig-25 fighter – and its thin skin would render it utterly vulnerable to a burst from the mighty Gatling gun.

Even heat-seeking SAM missiles are likely to miss the A-10. For its design effectively shields the heat from its rear-mounted en-gines.

Also, the highly sophisticated jets pro-duce no tell-tale trail of smoke. There are additional reasons for the unconventional

Right **An automatic ammunition loading system has reduced the rearm- ing turnaround time from three hours to 15 minutes. The A-10 is one of the cheapest, least complex and most easily maintained modern weapons systems deployed.**

arrangement of the engines.

They do not obstruct the pilot's field of view, and their position also minimizes the risk of their swallowing up foreign objects when the plane is forced to use a rough front-line airstrip.

As well as possessing a host of defensive features, the A-10 is a veritable flying armoury. Each plane carries 1,350 rounds of ammunition for the monster gun. As well as armour-piercing incendiary (API) shells, capable of slicing through the side of a tank like a knife through butter, the pilot can fire high-explosive (HE) rounds at soft-skinned targets. The projectiles are loaded in a continuous belt consisting of five API shells followed by one HE bullet, and so on. The pilot can fire at a rate of either 2,000 or 4,000 rounds per minute, typically in half-second bursts.

Backing up this devastating firepower is a whole host of other armaments – in all, a total of 7,257 kg of mixed ordnance on 11 pylon stations slung beneath the wings. These include both conventional and laser-guided weapons, such as rockets, cluster bombs, Hobo electro-optically guided heavy bombs and Maverick heat-seeking missiles. However, Maverick's future is uncertain: it is TV-guided, necessitating several seconds of relatively straight, level flight for the pilot to identify his target, lock the missile guidance system onto it, and fire the weapon. This inhibits the plane's manoeuvrability, which is such a vital element in the A-10's defensive and offensive strategies.

Damage to a smooth-skinned, sophisticated fighter during combat means intricate repairs at best, disaster at worst. But because the A-10 flies at subsonic speeds, it needs no smooth skin. It can limp home if necessary, riddled with holes like the heroic planes of World War II, though important components – including the pilot – will

have been protected by its tough armour. It can even land on a motorway and hide under an overpass while a mechanic simply rivets new plates onto the body from the outside. Since these panels are mostly of single curvature, any competent mechanic can easily bend a patch from a piece of sheet metal and rivet it in position.

When the repairs are completed, the pilot can go on ground alert with his communications systems driven by the auxiliary power unit, and be ready to respond to requests for air support from the front in minutes.

Biggest Wing in the West

The purpose of the A-10 is specific. If Russian tanks ever rolled west into Europe, the A-10s would be there to meet them. The 81st USAF Tactical Fighter Wing that flies the plane is the biggest in the West. Based at the neighbouring airfields of RAF Woodbridge and RAF Bentwaters in eastern England, the six squadrons, each consisting of 18 pilots, fly short missions to four Forward Operating Locations (FOLs) in Germany: at Semback, Leipheim, Noervenich and Ahlhorn.

The 81st works on the simple and effective principle of forward basing and rearward maintenance. The RAF bases in eastern England provide full maintenance facilities in sophisticated bomb-proof shelters. By contrast, the FOLs are austere places, with only 50 permanent personnel at each. Their sole function is to turn the planes round as fast as possible and get them airborne again. So far, the men have been able to solve all problems on the spot. Nevertheless, they still depend on a regular supply of spares, and this is provided by a C-130 Hercules transport plane, which flies out any necessary parts. With a combat radius of just over 450 km, the A-10s can fly to the border zone, operate for 1 hour 45

minutes, and return to their FOLs. Alternatively, they can go to temporary sites located only 40 km – less than five minutes' flying time – behind the front line and be back in the air to attack enemy tanks within about an hour.

Each A-10 pilot knows his way to eastern Europe flying by landmarks alone. This is just as well, because, characteristically, the A-10 lacks sophisticated, computerized navigation systems, though it is provided with a radar-controlled landing device and a 'head-up' system which gives the pilot basic flying information – airspeed, altitude and attitude of flight. Beyond these simple aids, the pilot is in total control of his aircraft and is responsible for finding his way unaided. In flight and fight, then, the emphasis is back where it used to be 25 years ago: on pure airmanship. Many pilots welcome the opportunity to rely on their skills.

A typical enemy encounter for an A-10 pilot would be an attack on a missile launching site. Two A-10s would share the task with two AH-1 Cobra helicopters. The helicopters, called in by ground and air liaison officers, first locate and identify the target, and then, lurking at treetop level, launch wire-guided missiles at the missile site and direct a laser beam at a specific target. The beam is dispersed by vegetation, but not by a solid object such as a missile launcher: it bounces off the target and is reflected back so that it shows up on an approaching A-10's underwing Pave Penny laser spot tracker. This gives the plane's pilot a red diamond shape on his head-up display at which he can aim his weapons. He opens fire at 1,200 m – distant enough to turn away sharply and come in for a second pass, without having to expose himself by flying over the target area.

Below **Exposed: the fastest-firing gun ever installed in an aircraft. Each one of the seven rotating barrels has its own bolt which rams, locks, fires, unlocks and extracts rounds during each revolution of the barrel cluster. Powered by double hydraulic motors, the gun has a double-ended linkless feed system. The 1,350 rounds are held within the huge storage drum by fixed partitions, being moved along them by the turning of an inner helix. At the forward end of the drum, the shells are transferred to a linkless conveyor. This carries live rounds to the gun and returns spent cases to be reinserted in the now-empty partitions.**

ROTATING HEAD BOLT

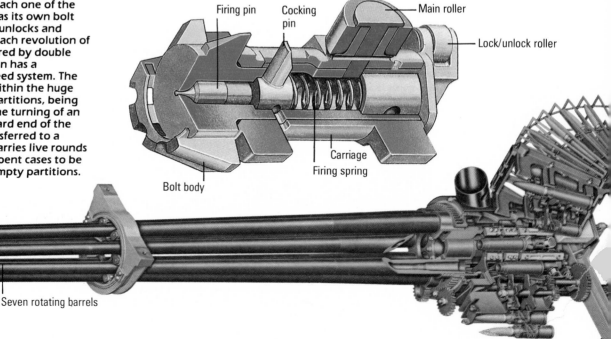

Firing pin

Cocking pin

Main roller

Lock/unlock roller

Carriage

Firing spring

Bolt body

Gun muzzle   Seven rotating barrels

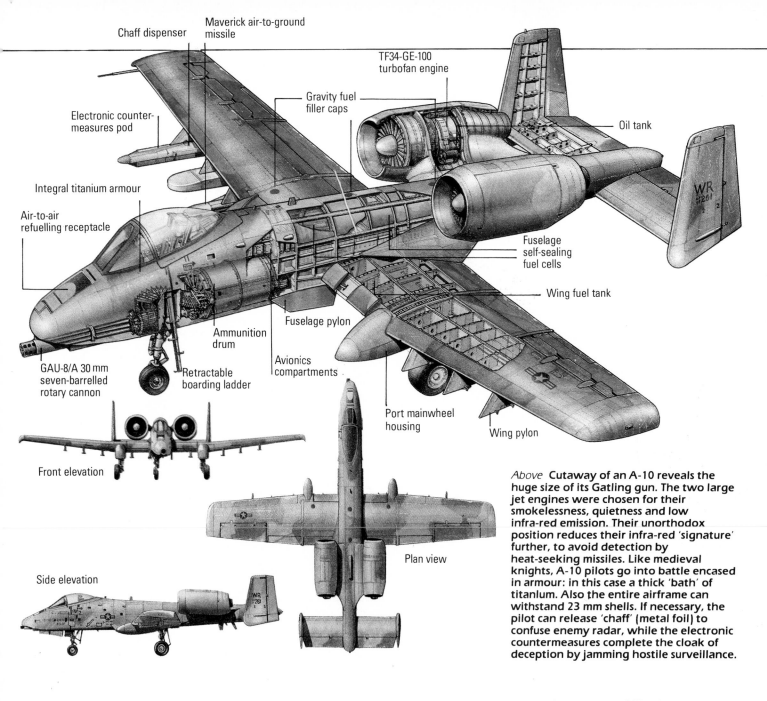

Chaff dispenser

Maverick air-to-ground missile

TF34-GE-100 turbofan engine

Oil tank

Electronic counter-measures pod

Gravity fuel filler caps

Integral titanium armour

Air-to-air refuelling receptacle

Fuselage self-sealing fuel cells

Wing fuel tank

GAU-8/A 30 mm seven-barrelled rotary cannon

Retractable boarding ladder

Ammunition drum

Fuselage pylon

Avionics compartments

Port mainwheel housing

Wing pylon

Front elevation

Side elevation

Plan view

Above **Cutaway of an A-10 reveals the huge size of its Gatling gun. The two large jet engines were chosen for their smokelessness, quietness and low infra-red emission. Their unorthodox position reduces their infra-red 'signature' further, to avoid detection by heat-seeking missiles. Like medieval knights, A-10 pilots go into battle encased in armour: in this case a thick 'bath' of titanium. Also the entire airframe can withstand 23 mm shells. If necessary, the pilot can release 'chaff' (metal foil) to confuse enemy radar, while the electronic countermeasures complete the cloak of deception by jamming hostile surveillance.**

GAU-8/A 30 mm GATLING GUN

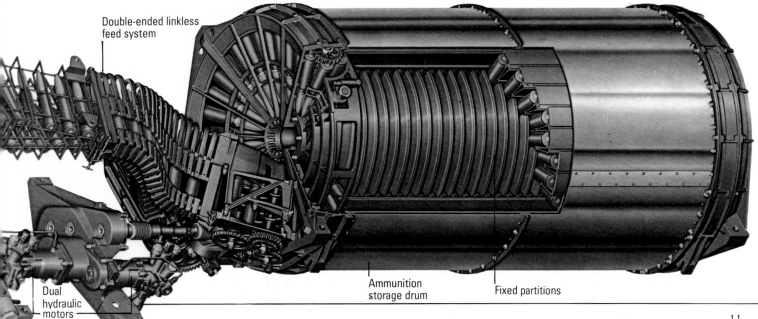

Double-ended linkless feed system

Dual hydraulic motors

Ammunition storage drum

Fixed partitions

FORWARD SWEEP FOR FIGHTERS' WINGS

If you want a fighter that goes faster on less power, dodges missiles, and doesn't fly like a brick at low speeds, just turn the wings round

Late in the 1980s the balance of power in the skies over Western Europe will change dramatically. For by then the US Air Force will be operating the first of a new generation of fighters, aircraft with forward-swept wings. Faster, lighter, more manoeuvrable than ever before these aircraft represent the nearest thing to the perfect warplane ever devised by Man.

Forward-swept wings get around two major problems. The first is compression – the faster an aircraft flies, the less time the air has to get out of its way. So instead of flowing smoothly over the wings and fuselage, it is suddenly compressed and forms a shock wave. A swept-back wing delays this compression and reduces the shock wave and resulting drag; a forward-swept wing reduces this drag even further.

The other problem is low-speed manoeuvrability and lift; the early swept-back wings made the aircraft virtually uncontrollable at low speeds; the wing tip would lose lift and stall before the wing root, creating major instability problems. These were also solved by forward-swept wings – and if the wing were curved upwards just slightly, not only would the root stall before the tip, but the lift would be distributed more evenly over the entire wing surface.

Something for nothing

With forward-swept wings, engines can be smaller and the weight less. Or, by keeping standard engines and aircraft sizes, performance can be very greatly improved. It was not the forward-swept wing and its composite structure that alone provided all the attraction. A pair of small wings in the nose improved the concept even more by deflecting air onto the wing root during tight turns, dives and while climbing. This further delays root stall and makes the aeroplane even more agile.

Grumman (who had already built the magnificent F-14 Tomcat fighter) were selected at the end of 1981 to build a demonstrator, using the forward fuselage of another lightweight fighter, the F-5, and the undercarriage of the F-16.

The FSW demonstrator has a wing span of 8.3 m, a length of 14.6 m and a take-off weight of 7,300 kg. It is powered by a 7,260 kg-thrust engine built by General Electric and has a digital control system to employ the advantages of a blended flight profile.

This means that the pilot can bob, weave, drift and skid to confuse anti-aircraft missiles while still making a controlled manoeuvre such as a turn or attack. With the marriage of forward-swept wings, composite materials and digital control systems, fighters of the future will take on the small, twisting missiles with a more than even chance of winning. Moreover, with greater lift for a given size, the forward-swept wing means the fighter needs less runway in a battle where long runways may not long remain intact.

Couple the FSW to a computerized electronic control system and you have all the best of any type of fighter the pilot needs in any type of combat. There has never been a safer bet than the future role of the fighter pilot and his powerful, diminutive machine.

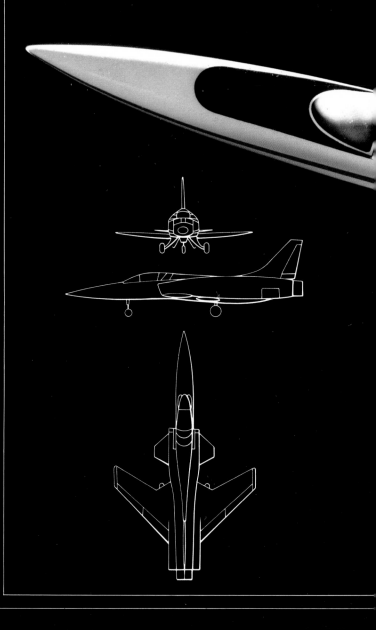

Below It looks dramatically different, but it offers something for nothing – Grumman's forward-swept wing (FSW) concept gives less drag, better low-speed handling, lower weight, and incredible agility. The small wings on the nose help tune the airflow over the main wings' roots during tight turns and dives and during take-off and landing. The concept would be unworkable without high-strength composites that have replaced steel and light alloys in aircraft construction. The aircraft uses the nose section from the existing Northrop F-5 (*left*) and the undercarriage of the General Dynamics F-16 (*right*). When the FSW concept reaches frontline service the majority of combat aircraft will become obsolete overnight.

HARRIER DISPERSED OPERATIONS
HARRIER DISPERSED OPERATIONS   Classical pattern

- ⬤ Unstocked sites
- ⬤ Pre-stocked sites
- ◯ Support sites

Aircraft disperse in emergency

Peacetime base

Forward edge of battle area (FEBA)

Return

Redeploy

Supply base

VL   STO

STO Unstocked site

Operation From Unstocked Sites

Rapid Reaction

Return   Return   Out

VTO Unstocked site

VL

Supply base

VL   STO   VL   STO   VL   VTO Unstocked site

Support site

THE HARRIER PASSES THE TEST

The Harrier had a lot to prove when it went into action, but prove itself it did. V/STOL works – and that's official

Operation From Pre-stocked & Support Sites

'The Harrier is probably the most misunderstood aircraft ever built – until it actually gets into a shooting war, no one, except those already operating it, will realise its full potential.' So said John Fozard, the former chief designer on the British Aerospace Harrier project. Twenty-two aircraft destroyed in air-to-air combat over the Falklands for no Harrier losses proves the point.

Had it not been for the foresight and determination of the Harrier design team, the Falklands might still be occupied, with much of the British Task Force at the bottom of the South Atlantic.

What is it about this remarkable aircraft that makes it so effective against fighters costing twice as much and flying twice as fast?

The answer is V/STOL which simply means Vertical/Short Take-Off and Landing. The process by which this gravity-defying form of flight is achieved is vectored thrust – one of Britain's not-so-secret weapons.

The key to the Harrier's vectored thrust is a unique power plant, the Rolls-Royce Pegasus. The Pegasus is a two-stage turbo-

Left **The Harrier, in its Royal Air Force role, combines the 'go-anywhere' versatility of a helicopter with the speed and striking force of a purpose-built fighter. 'Catch me if you can'** (*below*). **Any aircraft can be hidden in trees if a large enough clearing can be made – only the Harrier can land in that clearing, take off again, and carry out a mission.**

fan engine with a low bypass ratio of 1.4:1 and 21,500 lb of thrust, all of which is divided between the Harrier's four fuselage-mounted jet nozzles. It's the nozzles that do all the hard work in the Harrier as they swivel from an aft-facing direction to point downwards at an angle ten degrees forward of the vertical. The Pegasus engine is simple, robust and reliable, and with a thrust-to-weight ratio of nearly 6:1 it is one of the most efficient non-afterburning jet engines currently in service.

One feature of a turbofan engine that's not normally considered by most of the public is that much of the air coming out of the nozzles has not been burned. The turbofan operates on the principle that it is more efficient to move a lot of air slowly than a little air fast; the Pegasus is no exception. The low pressure compressor which draws air through the front of the engine is run off the low pressure turbine, which is itself driven by the engine's exhaust gases. The air drawn in by the compressor, however, doesn't all go through the engine's combustion chambers; 60% of it is channelled straight through the front nozzles, at a speed of 400 m/sec and a temperature of 110°C. The exhaust from the rear nozzles travels at 600 m/sec at a temperature of 635°C. Surprisingly, someone standing just ten metres away from a Harrier that's taking off vertically would be perfectly safe.

By comparison with the Pegasus engine, the Harrier airframe is remarkably conven-

tional: it is a fixed-wing, subsonic ground-attack/fighter which relies on agility and its unique V/STOL capability for survival.

Until the Falklands conflict the Harrier had been consistently underrated: several myths perpetuated the misconception that the Harrier was neither a bomber, fighter or ground attack aircraft – and certainly not a combination of any of these.

The first, and possibly most damaging myth was that vertical take-off wastes a lot of fuel. It doesn't: take-off requires about 50 kg of fuel; an equivalent fighter with an afterburner engine will use *at least* three times more fuel to get airborne.

The second myth is that the Harrier cannot lift its maximum payload from a vertical take-off. Actually, that's not a myth: the Harrier can only lift half its full load in vertical take-off. But the Harrier can do it almost from a ploughed field. No other aircraft (except for a helicopter) can lift a usable load from a minimum take-off run. In fact, without a reasonably long runway, very few aircraft would be able to take off at all.

Vertical take-off

Nevertheless, vertical take-off does pose some problems, so it tends only to be used where the tactical situation demands it. Far more common is a short take-off where the aircraft gets airborne at about 50 knots (nautical miles per hour) with the nozzle angled downwards at 50°. At 50 kts one third of the aircraft's weight is supported by the wings, so the engines don't have to work so hard for a given take-off weight.

One area where the Harrier scores above everything else sharing the sky with it is vertical landing: even in the worst weather a Harrier pilot can execute an approach to a small landing ground, hover for a few seconds, and then drop gently onto the landing pad. The Harrier still uses less fuel than any other aircraft during this manoeuvre. And there's no need for an emergency fuel supply in case the pilot overshoots or has to be diverted to another airfield because of bad weather – witness the Royal Navy's Sea Harriers in the South Atlantic; they were landing on the heaving decks of aircraft carriers that rose and fell by up to 5 m at a time, in visibility of 50 m.

And although the Harrier is capable of flying from a square of grass, a more permanent home for it can be built very simply by laying an aluminium mesh mat about 20 m square.

One of the factors that contributed to the success of the Falklands campaign was the 'ski-jump', a launching ramp fitted just over the bows of a light aircraft carrier. Using a 100 m take-off run with the ski-jump at the end of it, the Royal Navy's Sea Harriers were able to take off fully loaded and engage enemy aircraft in protracted dogfights without having to worry about their fuel or ammunition reserves.

Once in action the Harriers were devastating: agile, manoeuvrable and deadly – everything a fighter should be. The secret

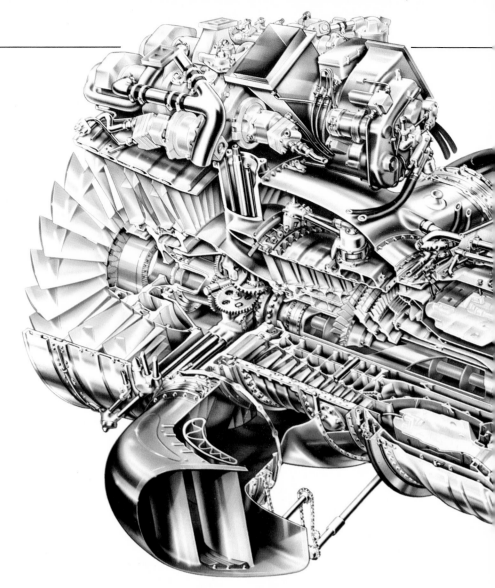

Above **The Rolls-Royce Pegasus Mk 104 engine of the Royal Navy's Sea Harriers is a light, tough, reliable design. The four nozzles swivel from an aft-facing direction to point downwards 10° in front of the vertical. On take-off it uses a third of the fuel a jet with afterburners would require, while developing enough power to push the plane up.**

Below **Nozzle control looks simple, but it accounts for much of the Harrier's performance. The nozzle control lever is next to the throttle lever and the two are juggled around on short and vertical take-off and vertical landing. With the nozzles angled to the rear at 50°, the Harrier will get airborne at just 50 kts, with a full load.**

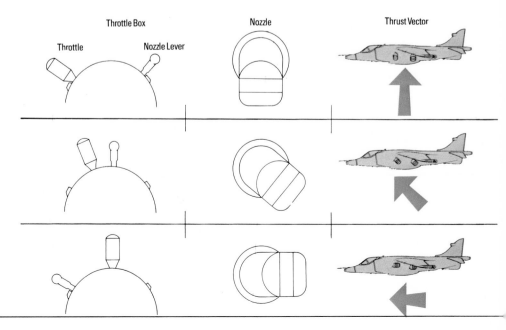

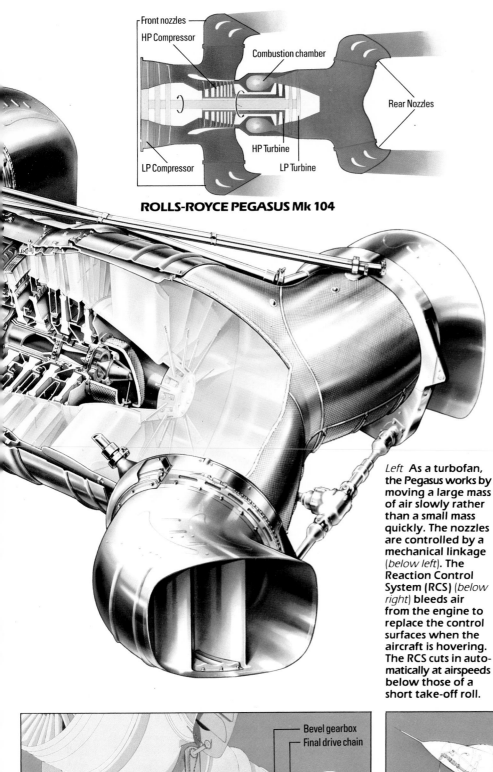

Front nozzles
HP Compressor
Combustion chamber
Rear Nozzles
HP Turbine
LP Compressor
LP Turbine

ROLLS-ROYCE PEGASUS Mk 104

Left **It's the rearmost nozzles that do most of the hard work – the front nozzles blow air drawn in by the low pressure compressor at the front, making the engine a turbofan.**

lay not so much in the airframe and weapons, excellent though they are, as in the way the pilots used their engines. 'Viffing' is the term used to describe what they did, and VIFF is an acronym of 'vectoring in forward flight'.

'Viffing'

What this means basically is that the pilots suddenly altered the direction of their engine nozzles to make the aircraft 'jump' out of the way of pursuing, faster enemy aircraft. But viffing goes a lot further than just getting out of someone's way – by altering the direction of the nozzles' thrust it is possible to turn more tightly, to pull out of dives more sharply and to enhance the natural agility of an already light aeroplane.

At low speeds the Pegasus engine also contributes to manoeuvrability. The aircraft's reaction control system (RCS) takes over from the ailerons and rudder: the RCS is an offshoot of the main engine, and bleeds air from the engine to the reaction control valves in the nose, tail and wingtips. The RCS cuts in automatically when the main engine nozzles turn downwards, and the RCVs work automatically in response to movements of the aircraft's controls.

One important point worth making here is that aerial dogfights do not necessarily require high speeds – criticism that the Harrier is too slow was again refuted by their operational record against supersonic Mirage aircraft over the Falklands. Dogfights generally take place at speeds of between 450 and 700 knots, well within the Harrier's range. Indeed flight trials where the Harrier was put against supersonic interceptors like the F-4 Phantom, F-14 Tomcat and F-15 Eagle resulted in a gratifying high number of 'kills' – up to 95% of all combat engagements.

As befits such a versatile aeroplane, the weapons fitted to the Harrier can be as varied as a mission requires. The Harrier can carry up to five tonnes of weapons, al-

Left **As a turbofan, the Pegasus works by moving a large mass of air slowly rather than a small mass quickly. The nozzles are controlled by a mechanical linkage** (*below left*). **The Reaction Control System (RCS)** (*below right*) **bleeds air from the engine to replace the control surfaces when the aircraft is hovering. The RCS cuts in automatically at airspeeds below those of a short take-off roll.**

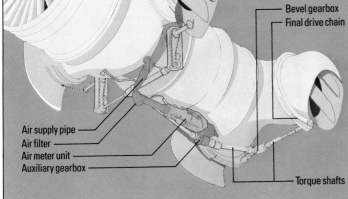

Bevel gearbox
Final drive chain
Air supply pipe
Air filter
Air meter unit
Auxiliary gearbox
Torque shafts

NOZZLE SYSTEM

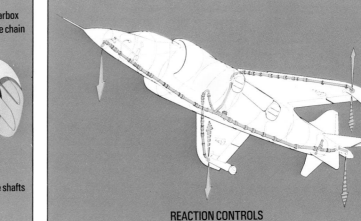

REACTION CONTROLS

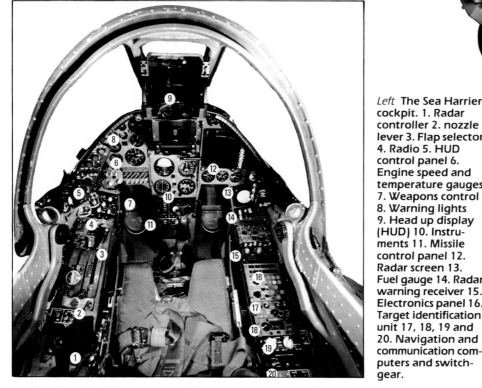

Left **The Sea Harrier cockpit. 1. Radar controller 2. nozzle lever 3. Flap selector 4. Radio 5. HUD control panel 6. Engine speed and temperature gauges 7. Weapons control 8. Warning lights 9. Head up display (HUD) 10. Instruments 11. Missile control panel 12. Radar screen 13. Fuel gauge 14. Radar warning receiver 15. Electronics panel 16. Target identification unit 17, 18, 19 and 20. Navigation and communication computers and switchgear.**

siderations in mind. The Harrier could be said to have evolved from the NATO defensive doctrine of 'Flexible response': match force with force, don't overreact, and above all prevent an escalation into nuclear war.

In its limited, tactical role, the Harrier is not a war-winner – unless it's a very small war. Used by the US Marines or the Royal Navy to support limited commando-style amphibious operations, it is an ideal tool for achieving control of local airspace in a small part of a wider battlefield.

New tactics

If the Harrier proved itself to a sceptical world-wide audience over the Falklands, it had already initiated a totally new tactical doctrine for the RAF in Europe and elsewhere. 'Elsewhere' really means Belize, Central America, where Britain maintains a small defence force to protect the local population from outside aggression. Part of that force is a flight of four Harriers. Tactically, Belize could be likened to an embattled Europe: in the event of a war the country's one airstrip would not last long, and there is no guarantee that the roads would be of any use to fast jets. So the Harrier flight operates on semi-war footing with the aircraft dispersed in hardened shelters away from the runway, from which they can fly vertical take-off and landing (VTOL) operations if necessary. Going a stage further, the Harriers can be landed in a clearing, hidden from prying eyes, to operate with impunity – and little chance of detection.

So far, no one has yet come close to imitating the Harrier. Many have tried – the Soviet airforce operate the YAK-36 Forger, Bell of the USA are experimenting with their XV-15 tilt-rotor aircraft – but the Harrier re-

though two and a half tonnes is a more usual load. The weapons range from 68 mm rockets carried in pods under the wings, AIM9-L Sidewinder air-to-air missiles, and old-fashioned 1,000 lb bombs. The US Marines use a version of the Mk 83 Snakeye, a 1,000 lb bomb with a laser-guided brain in the nose. This weapon relies for accuracy on a laser beam which is trained on the target by either a soldier on the ground, another aircraft or the Harrier itself. The 'brain' detects laser reflections from the target and simple steers towards it.

Another horrifyingly effective weapon cleared for use on the Harrier is the AGM-84A Harpoon anti-ship missile. Like the French Exocet, Harpoon is a sea-skimmer capable of blowing a ship in two. Add to this the two 30 mm Aden cannon carried by each aircraft, and the Harrier becomes a de-

vastatingly effective – and very cost-effective – piece of machinery.

One important facet of the Harrier's design concept is that it is a conventional fighter – it carries no nuclear or chemical weapons. In the strategic sense this is vitally important: the aircraft is designed to hold its own in a conventional battle, to successfully defend areas of tactical importance without resorting to the use of weapons of mass destruction.

If it can successfully do this, then it has raised the so-called 'nuclear threshold'; indeed, it has become a deterrent in its own right. Aggressors would think twice about fighting an air force equipped with aircraft that could cause such immense damage without suffering heavy losses.

The Harrier can't do all this on its own, of course; it has merely joined the ranks of aircraft designed with the same strategic con-

Above **The Sea Harrier is identical to the ordinary Harrier from the cockpit back. It needs to be, as well: pilots using the jet nozzles in dog fights put incredible strain on the airframe and wings. This process is known as 'VIFF', or vectoring in forward flight** (*right*). **By altering the vector of the jet nozzles, the pilot can turn more tightly than his adversaries and out-manoeuvre anything he comes close to even if they are flying faster.**

mains unique. The Forger uses no less than *three* engines – one to go forward, two to go up and down. And it can't do either short take-offs or viffs. The Bell tilt-rotor aircraft has twin propelled engines mounted on the wings. They rotate from the vertical to the horizontal, allowing vertical take-off and landing with a steady, smooth progression to forward flight.

One sector of the public who didn't need much convincing about the finer qualities of the Harrier concept were the US Marine Corps with their own air wing. The Harrier was, to them an ideal ground-support aircraft to be operated from land and ships, but needed a great deal of development. What the 'Grunts' needed was an aircraft with twice the range and twice the payload of the British version, so the British and US governments have initiated a joint programme of development by BAe and

McDonnell-Douglas of the USA. This next generation Harrier is known as the Harrier II and will be designated AV-8B in US Marine Corps service and GR Mk5 by the RAF. Although outwardly similar to the current Harrier, the AV-8B has been the beneficiary of a detailed redesign – the wings are made from graphite/epoxy composites and have much better lift characteristics. The wing allows more fuel to be carried, but is also far stronger: more weapons can be carried below it, and the aircraft can perform tighter turns.

New flap and air-intake designs allow better airflow over the wings and through the engine, while a redesigned undersurface improves vertical take-off performance.

To augment these improvements the Pegasus engine is being developed to produce about 900 kg more thrust. This is

being done very simply by redesigning and reblading the low pressure compressor to increase the air flow by about 4.5 per cent. The only other changes necessary are detail modifications to strengthen the engine. But perhaps the most significant improvement to come is the development of a supersonic version of the Harrier. Rolls-Royce have already built a prototype engine, and British Aerospace are known to be working on a series of airframe studies. When the supersonic Harrier does get off the ground (some time in the late 1980s, it is hoped) its enemies are in for an even harder time. A US Marine Corps pilot put it this way: 'One day you'll jump a Harrier pilot – then we've got you!'

BOMBS FROM THE BLUE

Thanks to Stealth technology bombers have a far better chance of reaching their targets

In a secret location known only as 'The Ranch', some 45 km north-west of Las Vegas in the deserts of Nevada, US scientists and aircraft design teams have developed what may turn out to be the most influential ingredient in any future war. For what they have done is to provide a set of technology innovations that make aircraft almost invisible to radar and, thereby, virtually immune to attack. It is not science fiction. It is fact. And it is happening with several aircraft designs supporting new fighter and bomber projects for the US Air Force of the 1990s.

It all began when, in 1954, US Air Force General Curtis Le May called for designs that could produce a replacement for the Boeing B-52, then having flown only two years previously and scheduled to enter service as a bomber for conventional and nuclear weapons in 1955. After a long series of design competitions, where most of America's aviation industry came up with different ideas, the B-70 was selected as the best proposal. Development got under way late in 1957 and the aircraft began to take shape. But what emerged seven years later was just the opposite to what the Air Force wanted, for in that brief period the role and operating environment

of the big strategic bomber had changed completely.

Recognizing the significant lead in long range bombers held by the United States, the Soviet Union put a huge effort into developing a range of defensive mechanisms by which Russian airspace could be protected during any war that might break out

in the future. These comprised extensive defence radars scanning the long frontiers, numerous high speed interceptor aircraft, and a very large number of surface-to-air missile (SAM) sites, making it virtually impossible to penetrate the screen. Radar had become increasingly important for not only detecting the presence of a force attacking Soviet territory but also for guiding fighters in the defence. This was more important than for any other country because Russia's borders are the most extensive on Earth and visual recognition of attacking aircraft was a luxury placed firmly back in the Battle of Britain.

The relevance this had for the B-70 programme lay in the design specification that played the biggest part in shaping the aircraft's contours. The Air Force said they wanted a high-flying, Mach 3 bomber capable of dropping nuclear bombs on targets deep inside the Soviet Union.

To get to the astonishing speed of Mach 3, the B-70 carried six huge engines in a special section under the delta wing, with a massive intake protruding forward under the narrow fuselage. The aircraft weighed more than 200 tonnes in flight and its six mighty engines gave it a thrust of more than 75 tonnes, compared with 52 tonnes

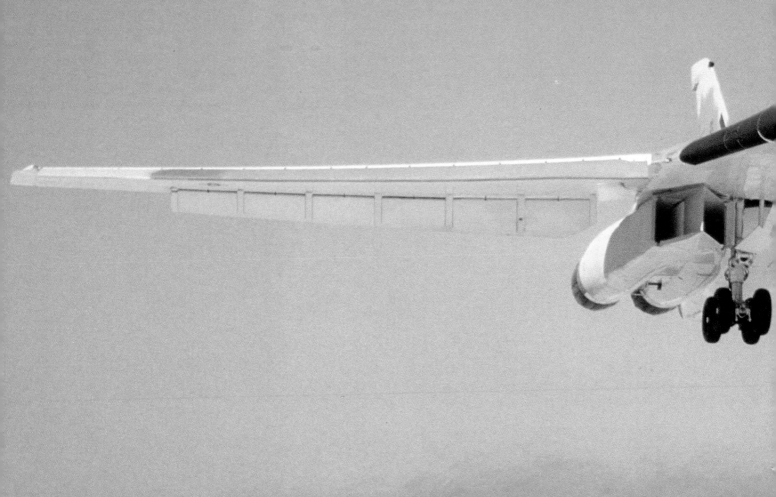

The Rockwell B1 bomber – the stealth concept has provoked a complete reappraisal of the conventional manned bomber aircraft as a tactical weapons delivery system.

Right **How not to do it. The B-52 has a radar profile like a barn door. The drones under its wings, however, are nearly invisible to radar; many have been used over China and Vietnam. The B-1** (*above*) **is nearer the mark. Its blended wing and fuselage and defensive avionics make it a formidable intruder at low level with a radar profile like a fighter aircraft.**

Right **The B-70 was the wrong aircraft at the wrong time. One possible Stealth design** (*far right*) **points the way. A Stealth mission might look like this** (*above*). *1.* **Low level approach while invisible to enemy aircraft.** *2.* **IMP shows which atmospheric layers give least radar range.** *3.* **Invisible approach.** *4.* **Jammers on for the attack. Escape flight would be similar.**

for the B-52 and 35 tonnes for the British Vulcan. With these powerplants, the B-70 could fly at a height of more than 22 km and keep a constant speed of Mach 3 (nearly 3000 km/h). But in every other respect it was a white elephant. Radar reflections from the B-70 would have been worse than for any other aircraft in the USAF inventory. The pronounced leading edge of the delta would have given a bright reflection, and the huge intake box slung under the centre fuselage would have looked several times its size on a radar screen. As for the engine exhausts, they would have given a clear and well-shaped image both to the defence radars and to infra-red sensors looking for hot intruders.

What was needed by the late 1960s was an aircraft capable of flying fast at low altitude, with a high-altitude dash capability to escape homing or guided missiles after dropping its bombs. From a study originated in 1965, the B-1 bomber emerged in the mid-1970s as the aircraft which stood the best chance of surviving a penetration mission. The engine intakes were still under the moulded wing/fuselage fairing but the

aircraft was designed from the outset to fly very low and very fast and sneak in under the radar screens before dashing to its target at Mach 0.85 (85 per cent of the speed of sound, or about 1040 km/h at sea level) no more than 60 metres above the ground.

Around the middle of the 1970s, however, a rather more radical solution to the problem appeared. *Stealth* began to seem a real possibility. It was not a single technical breakthrough but rather a synthesis of several different technologies, all of which came to fruition at the same time.

First, by giving up a lot of the performance that modern aerodynamic design can provide, an aircraft can be shaped to present a very small radar cross-section, or RCS. By deliberately going for a shape guaranteed to give a poor radar reflection the bomber need not necessarily seek the speed or low-altitude flight made necessary by its visibility. With engine intakes placed above the wings rather than below, by rounding the aircraft's curvature, specifically avoiding box-shaped protruberances or housings, and by moulding the wing and

fuselage into a blended 'lifting-body', the aircraft itself becomes difficult to detect. With engines designed and built for low heat emission signatures, exhaust outlets cowled for low radar reflections and a new philosophy for flying and performing attack missions, Stealth takes on the first of three unique capabilities never before assembled into one aeroplane.

Countermeasures

A second Stealth feature is the use of passive avoidance systems and active electronic countermeasures (ECM) designed to jam enemy radars. The passive element is fast becoming a mandatory feature of all combat aircraft and involves the use of highly sensitive detectors searching in every direction at once for the enemy radar beams looking for the attacking aircraft. The British firm Ferranti have developed a system called IMP which, linked to a cockpit computer, provides the crew with information allowing the aircraft to be flown around the defence radar screens thereby reducing the likelihood of detection. Active countermeasures are more sophisticated

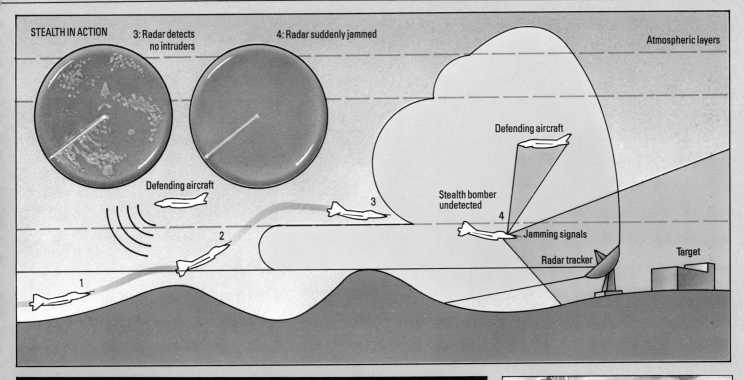

STEALTH IN ACTION

3: Radar detects no intruders

4: Radar suddenly jammed

Atmospheric layers

Defending aircraft

Defending aircraft

Stealth bomber undetected

Jamming signals

Radar tracker

Target

than ever before and have their part to play if the aircraft is picked up by radar.

The third Stealth feature is the use over the aircraft's entire surface of a low reflectivity absorber such as carbon-fibre or other composite materials. By absorbing the radar signal and dissipating the energy as heat the signal is weakened even further. This is one of the less sophisticated Stealth technologies and could include a large range of commercial materials otherwise used for such mundane tasks as insulating co-axial electric cables. The convergence of new operating requirements, which reduced the need for high speed at high altitude (or even high speed at low altitude), and the evolution of design and technology trends has made Stealth a reality at last, promising to introduce a generation of aircraft looking very different from those of today's airforces.

Secret flights

The new Stealth shapes began flying as early as 1977 with Boeing, Grumman, Lockheed and Northrop all involved at various levels of effort. The early test models, flown and tested at Nellis Air Force Base in Nevada, were about the size of a small fighter, with extensive trials leading to future designs for definitive aircraft. Lockheed has had many years' experience with Stealth-type technology and has developed a series of supersonic drones called GTD-21. Nearly 40 were built and some have been operated over China and Vietnam. They carry basic Stealth principles in their design and a few have been used in experiments with the four small Lockheed test aircraft.

Super bomber

Under the secret *Have Blue* Stealth fighter programme, from the Defence Advanced Projects Research Agency the US Defence Department is buying twenty Covert Survivable In-Weather Reconnaissance/Strike (CSIRS) aircraft which are expected to be in service by 1984. These will contribute a wealth of valuable operating experience as well as show the way for the biggest Stealth project of them all. Under a $7,300 million spending plan, Northrop is building a full-scale prototype of the Advanced Technology Bomber, the ATB, in-

corporating every Stealth feature in the book. It is being built, with support from Boeing and Vought, as a replacement for the B-1 bomber, which as described earlier goes only some of the way toward suppressing its radar visibility.

In a building not too far from Los Angeles Airport, Northrop has the ATB under wraps. It has a blended body-wing shape with a gently swept flying wing contour and small double fins on the trailing edge. Engine exhaust is cooled through a by-pass stage to a vented orifice at the back, the engine and intake assembly lying deep inside a gently flared intake with large, rounded lips. The forward section of the small, bulbous fuselage is smooth without the conventional window step and the entire aircraft is covered in radar-absorbent materials. The ATB should by flying by 1988 and the Air Force could have the first of at least 100 in service by 1991. It is like nothing else on Earth, the first in a series of futuristic shapes that will change the way men fly to war for decades to come.

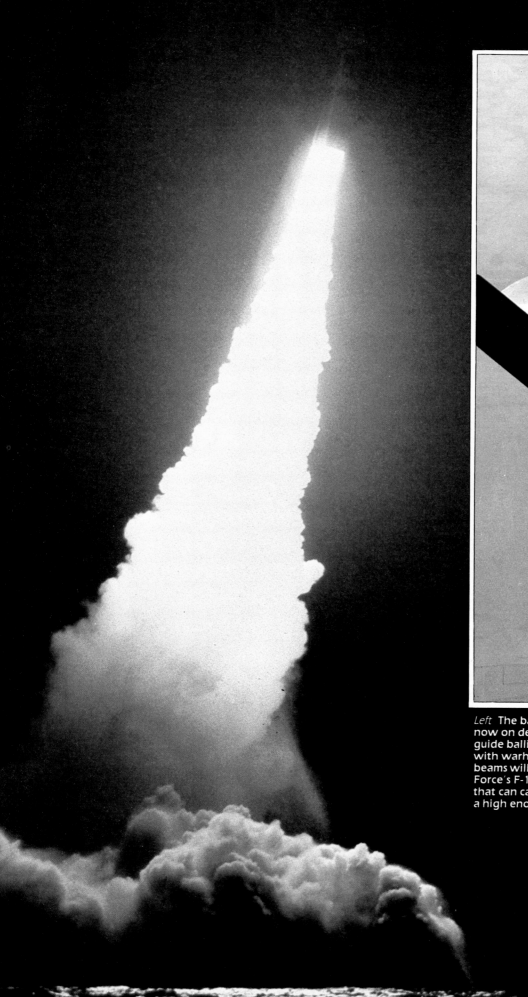

Left The balance of terror depends as much now on destroying the satellites which guide ballistic missiles as matching warhead with warhead. Killer satellites and laser beams will do that job, and so will the US Air Force's F-15 (*above*), a high-flying aircraft that can carry an anti-satellite missile into a high enough orbit to 'blind' the enemy.

WINNING TODAY'S STAR WARS

Tomorrow's wars will be lost or won in space — before the soldiers fire a shot in anger. Laser beams, killer satellites and 'eyes in the sky' may sound like science fiction, but they are very hard facts

From deep in the Cheyenne Mountains, the US Air Force's Consolidated Space Operations Center (CSOC) commands the high ground, waiting for a war no one wants. From dimly lit rooms where a dozen consoles flicker their tiny lights of warning and alarm, the space frontier is scanned minute by minute for signs of a ballistic missile attack, or of a Russian killer satellite rocketing through the void toward a vulnerable US reconnaissance satellite. At secret airfields many miles away, twin-tailed F-15 Eagle fighters wait for the order to take off. Be-

neath their bulbous fuselages are slim, pointed projectiles that if released will home on the killersats and blow them to fragments. This is not science fiction. It is here today. It is the new reality of that eternal search for command of the ultimate high ground.

For twenty years the US Air Force has been building a presence in space that now makes the outcome of war on Earth dependant on the success, or failure, of watching eyes from space. From several dozen different points around the globe, and from distances as far out as 35,500 km or as close as 150 km, military satellites control the instruments of war that lie waiting in deep undergound silos or far beneath the surface of the ocean. They are a fundamental part of the way any future war will be fought and they are the new way military control of territory on Earth will be exercised.

The vital importance of military satellites means that no country that has them can afford to let them be destroyed. But while Britain maintains its own military communication satellites, and European NATO forces use their own satellites for transferring messages, only the super-powers have the full spectrum of space equipment that brings a new dimension to war.

Tomorrow's battlefield

The Russians launch about 80 military satellites each year. More than half of them are on reconnaissance missions with powerful telescopic cameras that return their information to Earth in packages or send down TV pictures of the Earth below. Other satellites are designed to swoop low above the top of the atmosphere and eavesdrop on radio messages from enemy forces below.

Then there are the military weather satellites — quite separate from the civilian Metsats that bring the evening weather picture on television. Military satellites give detailed profiles of the atmosphere, close examination of cloud layers, and even a view of what is happening *under* the clouds. That information is important — aircraft and ships at sea use the weather to hide an attack or gain advantage over the enemy.

Weather information over the enemy's territory is also needed if conventional war ever gives way to nuclear conflict. On the battlefield the prevailing wind would work to the advantage of the attacking forces if radiation drifted over enemy territory, causing them to take protective measures that would slow a retreat or cause confusion.

And then there are the big communication satellites in stationary orbit. Soldiers on the ground could maintain contact over great distances through the Comsats in space, and ships would communicate with each other by this link too. But the majority of commands going through space would control the bombers flying over the North Pole to Soviet Russia.

To warn of attack, neither America nor

Russia rely exclusively any more on the big listening radars strung out along the great continental arcs. The first line of warning has to be the satellites because they are less vulnerable and look down from stationary orbit with unblinking eyes on the Earth below. Thus, the famous four minute warning is now at least a 15 minute opportunity for the power under attack to release its missiles before the falling warheads destroy the means of retaliation.

That fifteen minutes is now the basis of deterrence (sometimes known as MAD – Mutually Assured Destruction). Without eyes in space, technology would have overtaken the principle of nuclear stalemate. It would just, conceivably, be possible for an aggressor to risk attack by striking first in the almost certain knowledge that he could destroy the enemy's nuclear missiles before they could be fired. But all that has been avoided with the military early-warning satellites in orbit. Instead, if

Right **First find your satellite . . . The stationary orbit is full of potential targets some 36,000 km away. These are the hardest to destroy because they are the hardest to reach. Massive communications satellites** (*below*) **might be destroyed by shrapnel from a near miss, but perhaps lasers and particle beams are the best answers?**

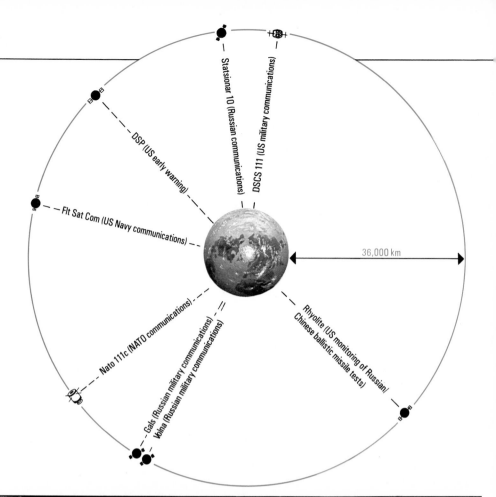

Statsionar 10 (Russian communications)

DSCS 111 (US military communications)

DSP (US early warning)

Flt Sat Com (US Navy communications)

36,000 km

Nato 111c (NATO communications)

Gals (Russian military communications)
Volna (Russian military communications)

Rhyolite (US monitoring of Russian/Chinese ballistic missile tests)

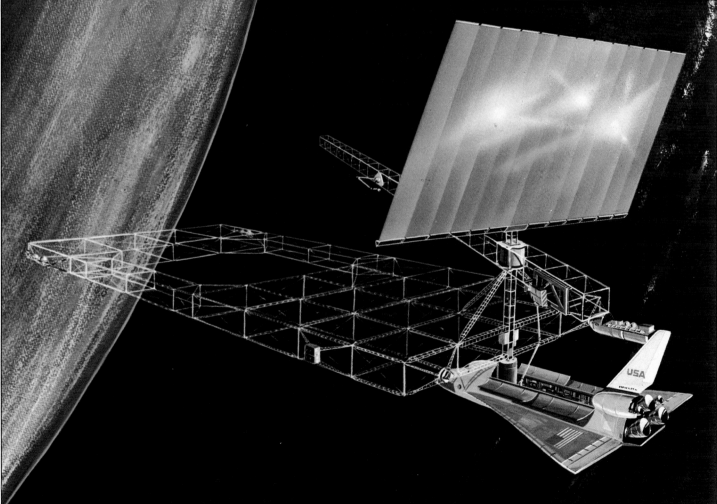

the satellites themselves ever came under attack, this could signal the start of a massive strike against the strategic deterrent. But there is more at stake than that alone. The most important satellites of all are for navigating the 'nukes' – the ballistic missiles – on their way to their respective targets.

Missile targeting is now so accurate that the capability of the guidance equipment exceeds the best information available about exactly where the target point is. This means that as the missile flies to its target it must consult a satellite, which can measure the respective positions of both projectile and target, updating the former with information about the latter. By the early 1990s, all America's big missiles launched from silos or submarines would talk to navigation satellites (Navsats). Moreover, successive generations of cruise missile would also receive information from the Navsats and fly even more precisely to their destinations.

The important point about this impending vulnerability is that if an enemy ever seriously believed he could knock out the satellites which form so vital a part of defence operations he could decide to risk a first strike.

The Russians began to test different types of anti-satellite device in the mid-1960s, shortly after the Americans had shown the feasibility of hitting ballistic missiles in space.

The Russians began to experiment with killersats – killer satellites which intercept and destroy enemy satellites in space. That prompted the US Air Force to develop a quick response and, rather than evolve its own killersat, engineers resurrected an old project devised to destroy incoming ballistic missiles.

Shoot 'em down!

In its new form, two rocket stages would be attached to a special, drum-shaped, impact device. Once launched from under the fuselage of a fighter flying at 20-25,000 m the two-stage rocket would curve up and out of the atmosphere, propelling the impact head toward the enemy satellite, but at such a speed that the impact would blow the satellite to pieces.

The Russian method required a killersat to be put in orbit first, far below the target satellite, and then either to be shot straight up on a collision course or to pepper the target with shrapnel when it was blown up from less than 1 km away. The latter method has been seen to work, although the target satellites have always been put in space first by the Russians.

But the US still seems to be at a disadvantage: the F-15 anti-satellite impact head can only reach comparatively low objects, like the Soviet ocean surveillance satellites that would be used in war to guide submarine-launched missiles flying low on depressed trajectories. The higher flying satellites, like the reconnaissance types or the stationary orbit satellites for communication or early warning, need something different. That 'something' may be a family of directed energy weapons, like lasers and particle-beam devices built to send bolts of energy in either single or continuous waves of destructive power capable of burning through steel.

The Russians have shown considerable ability in the development of lasers, and experimental establishments inside the Soviet Union are known to have used nuclear explosions, contained by enormous bell-shaped chambers, to generate massive quantities of electrical energy to discharge through a laser. The Americans have done preliminary studies on the possibility of sending into orbit laser or particle-beam weapons of enormous power, sufficient to 'zap' satellites or missiles several hundred kilometres away. The technological problems with this type of weapon are enormous but so are the rewards for developing it – and the race may be over sooner than we think. The Russians are already fitting lasers to their frigates to hit and destroy fast, sea-skimming missiles like *Exocet* before they reach their targets.

If war in space, with 'death rays' and killersats, seems just a little far-fetched, don't be fooled. The scientists and military men are in deadly earnest. 'Nobody wants to have to fight a war, but that doesn't mean you shouldn't try to win' is a widely held view nowadays in the corridors of military power.

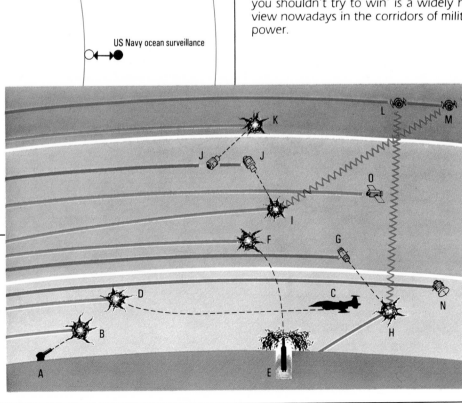

Orbit height (km) 1,000   10,000   100,000

Vela (US nuclear test monitoring)

Nav Star (US navigation)

DMSP Block 5D (US military weather)

US Navy ocean surveillance

KH-11 (CIA reconnaissance)

Russian reconnaissance

Big Bird (USAF reconnaissance)

LASP (USAF reconnaissance)

Above and *right* **Low earth orbits will be the battlefield in space. This scenario shows how ground-based lasers, aircraft and missiles (A, C and E) would attack enemy Reconsats, Metsats and Navsats (B, D and F). Reconsats and Navsats (N and O) threatened by enemy killer-sats (H and I) would be destroyed by Laser Battlesats and gunships (G and J) under the guidance of early warning satellites (L and M). Another Battlesat (J) destroys an enemy communications satellite (K) that is in stationary orbit above the battlefield.**

27

SEA WAR

As the Falklands War demonstrated, today's highly sophisticated missile systems have come to dominate maritime warfare. Faster than sound, hard to detect and harder to deflect, the anti-ship missile can destroy its target with a single hit. Against such a threat, the best defence remains 'portable air superiority' — the aircraft carrier, able to control airspace (and sea) for many miles around a surface fleet

Ships of the British Task Force deploying stores during the 1982 Falklands campaign.

DEATH ON THE OCEAN WAVES

Sea skimming missiles are the new thing in sea warfare. They are deadly, horribly effective and can only be stopped by super-expensive computer firing systems

'Take cover!' Those were very nearly the last words of Captain 'Sam' Salt, RN. Three or four seconds later his ship, HMS *Sheffield*, took a direct hit from an Exocet AM39 missile. Lunging towards the doomed destroyer at nearly 1100 km/h, just 2.5 m above the surface of the South Atlantic, the missile was unstoppable. It struck the *Sheffield* amidships, just above the waterline, smashed a hole in her side and started an uncontrollable fire. Within minutes HMS *Sheffield* had ceased to exist as a warship: five hours later she was a smoking hulk, abandoned and adrift.

The Argentinian pilot who fired the missile never saw the result of his handiwork — he launched the weapon from 50 km away,

well over the horizon. Whether he knew it or not, he had just ushered in a new era of naval warfare. It was the first time an Exocet missile had been used in anger and the first time, indeed, that any sea-skimming missile had seen action in a major conflict. The results were devastating, with numbing implications for every navy in the world. Things would never be the same at sea again.

Anti-ship missiles have been in use since Germany deployed them during World War 2. Later, the Egyptians and Israelis regularly sank each other's ships with one form of missile or another. But the sea-skimmer was a new arrival.

Whereas a high-flying missile — especially

one big enough to sink a ship — can be tracked by radar and shot down like an aeroplane, the sea-skimmer's survival technique is daunting. For a start, it flies so close to the surface that its radar image is reflected from the water to create a 'mirror effect' — the target's radar sees two missiles and cannot tell which is the real one. On top of that, the radar picks up 'clutter' from the wave-tops, echoes that come and go constantly, blurring the image even more. Finally, most anti-aircraft guns and missiles are designed to fire in to the air and not at the surface. So when French missile manufacturers Aerospatiale decided to build a cheap but effective sea-skimming missile, they were backing a winner.

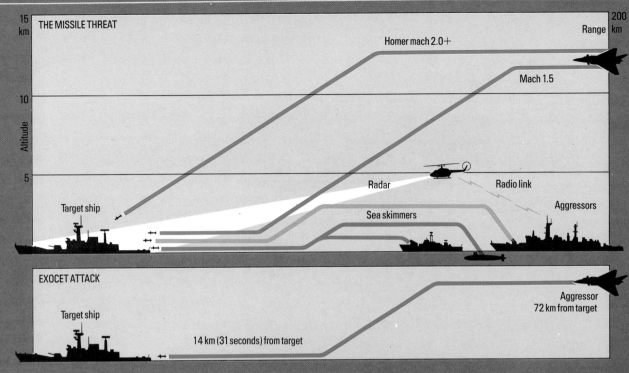

THE MISSILE THREAT

15 km — Altitude — 10 — 5

200 km — Range

Homer mach 2.0+

Mach 1.5

Target ship — Radar — Radio link — Aggressors — Sea skimmers

EXOCET ATTACK

Target ship

14 km (31 seconds) from target

Aggressor 72 km from target

The Exocet missile is some 5.2 m long, 350 mm in diameter, and has a 1 m wingspan. Its guidance system must be fed with the bearing and range of the target, and the height it must fly above the water, but once the missile is launched, the operator can forget about it — it will find its own way to the target. Once launched, from a ship, aircraft or land base, Exocet's rocket motor takes it up to a speed of Mach 0.93 while the missile dives to wave-top height. A sensitive radio altimeter bounces radio signals off the water below to give an instantaneous readout of height and immediate response to extra-large waves. Normal cruise height is about 2.5 m above the water, but in rough weather — like that encountered in the South Atlantic — the operator can dial in a substantially higher cruise altitude.

Exocet has an inertial navigation system — it knows exactly where it was when it was launched, and uses this information to work out when it is within 14 km of the target — the point at which it automatically

switches on its radar scanner. The scanner detects the target, works out how far off course the missile is (in the two or three minutes since it was launched, the target ship might have moved as much as 3 km) and then points it in the right direction. Just 31 seconds later, 165 kg of high explosive hit the centre of the ship. If the missile doesn't get a direct hit, however (astute seamanship and fast reactions can 'fox' the missile), a proximity fuse will set the warhead off close enough to cause major damage to the superstructure and deck equipment.

An alternative method of attack is used by the Italian 'Otomat' missile. This is about the same size as Exocet, but uses a rocket booster to launch it and then a ramjet engine to cruise. With a similar guidance system to that of Exocet, it flies into the target area at low level seeking out its target with radar. When it is too close to be stopped it swoops up to a height of 175 m and dives onto the lightly protected upper decks.

The Israeli 'Gabriel', flying at 10 m above the sea, is command-guided for part of its

Below To protect small ships the Seawolf system has been designed with a special lightweight launcher: this can be loaded from below deck, so successive salvos can be fired without exposing personnel. *Bottom* The Seawolf in flight.

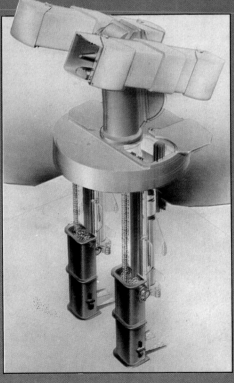

Far left Exocet missiles can be fired from ships, homing in on their targets with deadly accuracy. Difficult to intercept, they skim just above the surface of the waves. *Centre* The French Super Etendard aircraft carrying Exocet missiles makes a formidable opponent. *Left* The Sea Eagle, Britain's answer to the Exocet. It is intended to arm RAF Buccaneer aircraft.

Right Anatomy of a missile: Sea Skua is a compact, highly accurate weapon intended to hit the target, not just to explode nearby.
1. Fixed rear fins
2. Boost motor
3. Motor ignition delay unit 4. Sustainer motor 5. Gyros and gas bottle 6. Altimeter 7. Electronics pack 8. Control wing motor activators
9. Thermal batteries
10. Moving control wings 11. Warhead and safety arming unit 12. Homing head electronics 13. Homing head 14. Boost motor nozzle 15. Sustainer motor nozzle. Unlike Exocet, Sea Skua was not intended to be launched from a surface ship.

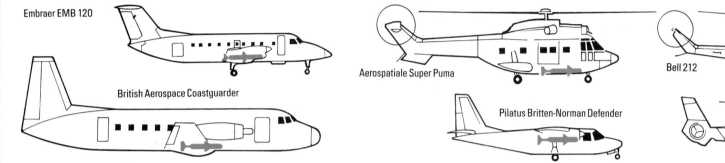

Solid propellant boost

Solid propellant sustainer motor

Control system

Embraer EMB 120

British Aerospace Coastguarder

Aerospatiale Super Puma

Bell 212

Pilatus Britten-Norman Defender

SEA SKUA ATTACK

flight. Exact details are, understandably, lacking but it is known that the missile can be controlled by an operator until it is close enough to the target not to be deflected by electronic counter-measures or jamming. In one role the missile uses semi-active homing – it detects radio and radar emissions from the target and follows them to their source. Electronic counter-measures aimed at confusing the missile are unlikely to be effective as the operator can program the missile to attack the source of any jamming waves. It is even rumoured that one type of 'Gabriel' has a TV camera in the nose.

Probably the most formidable missile in current service is the Soviet SS-N-3 'Shaddock'. About 13 metres long it is launched by two rocket boosters and then uses a ramjet engine to cruise at supersonic speed. Radar guidance is used for the initial portion of the flight, but the actual homing system is not known with any certainty in the West – it is believed that there are various

Above Designed to counter the threat from fast patrol craft before they get close enough to use their own weapons, Sea Skua is the only sea-skimming missile to be launched from helicopters. The Sea Skua uses Ferranti Seaspray radar to illuminate its target. It has excellent over-the-horizon attack capability. *Right* The Sea Skua proved its capabilities in the South Atlantic by crippling many ships.

THE SEA SKUA

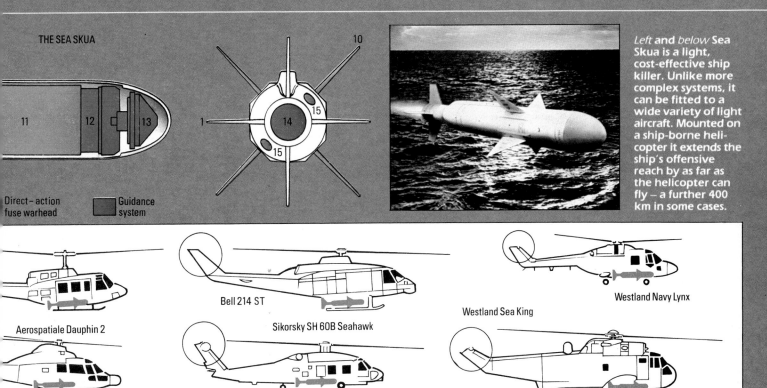

Direct–action fuse warhead

Guidance system

Left and **below** Sea Skua is a light, cost-effective ship killer. Unlike more complex systems, it can be fitted to a wide variety of light aircraft. Mounted on a ship-borne helicopter it extends the ship's offensive reach by as far as the helicopter can fly – a further 400 km in some cases.

Aerospatiale Dauphin 2

Bell 214 ST

Sikorsky SH 60B Seahawk

Westland Sea King

Westland Navy Lynx

versions all using different systems. What is certain is that the weapon has 'over-the-horizon' capability, with a maximum range of about 850 km; by comparison, Exocet, Otomat and Gabriel, with a 50-70 km range, are minute.

How, then to guard against these weapons which appear (apparently from nowhere) at high speed, close to the sea, and which present a very small target from their head-on approach? The primary defence, of course, is to spot the ship or aircraft which is intending to launch the missile and deal with it before it does so, but this is not always possible. So the emphasis today is on 'last ditch' close-in protection. The requirement is that the defensive system must detect the missile no closer than 2000 metres from the ship and then destroy it before it gets within 100 metres. With a Shaddock missile moving at Mach 2, this means that the reaction time is measured in seconds, not minutes.

There are two options: gun systems or missile systems. The Royal Navy has opted for missile systems and uses 'Seawolf', developed by British Aerospace from the well-known 'Rapier' land-based anti-aircraft missile. The detection system gives a one-second reaction time and the missile automatically flies into, and then along, the guiding radar beam. Its position is compared with that of the incoming missile, course corrections are calculated by computer and the missile intercepts the target. Trials showed that Seawolf was fast and agile enough to catch and destroy a 4.5 inch gun shell in flight and it will cope with missiles flying at speeds above Mach 2.

The gun solution is exemplified by the American 'Phalanx' system which uses radar to direct a multiple-barrel 20 mm Gatling gun towards the missile. This pours out a stream of 20 mm shells at 3000 rounds per minute, and the laws of chance practically guarantee a hit. But there are

doubts as to whether 20 mm shells do sufficient damage; even if the missile's controls are destroyed, it may still have enough momentum to hit the warship. Designers are working therefore on systems with heavier guns which will blow the missile apart. The Swiss 'Contraves Seaguard' system uses four 25 mm cannon, as does the Oerlikon 'Sea Zenith', while the German/Dutch 'Goalkeeper' uses four 30 mm Mauser cannon. All use fast-reaction radars and computers to direct the guns toward the incoming missile, and all have a rate of fire of about 300 rounds per barrel per minute.

At the moment the balance is fairly even between attacker and defender. But there are signs that the missile designers are working towards even faster missiles and this suggests that the gun and missile defence systems may well be stretched to their utmost in the future. The next stage in defence, though, has already been broached: the laser. The defence of high-value warships appears to be the most cost-effective way of employing laser beam weapons, and their reaction time is such that a laser can deliver its energy on a target almost 200 metres away while a Mach 6 hypersonic missile has travelled no more than a couple of centimetres. At present there are difficulties with weather and propagation of laser energy at long ranges, but these will be overcome in due course. And after the laser, the charged particle beam weapon is the next step. This promises all-weather performance, the instantaneous destruction of missiles and the ability to engage a number of targets with milliseconds of delay.

Above Ikara is a long-range anti-sub system. It comprises a guided missile launched from a ship that delivers homing torpedoes. *Left* Torpedo dropping position is computed by the ship. Once in the sea it homes in on target.

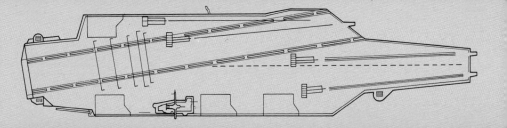

FORTRESS AFLOAT

The carrier is equally capable in a strategic assault role or as a flag-waving visitor to distant trouble spots. To those without understanding of its capabilities and limitations, however, it is a handicap with little value

The traditional aircraft carrier, able to pack almost 100 aircraft and stay at sea for several months, is expensive to build and operate. Not surprisingly, these massive flat-tops have always been first in line for disposal to effect reductions in defence expenditure, because they have long been considered an outmoded type of warship. History proves otherwise. Today, strategists are once again welcoming the carrier as a formidable fortress afloat.

In considering the vulnerability of large surface vessels, the Soviet naval forces watched with interest when a Soviet SS-N-2A missile sank the Israeli destroyer *Eilath*. The point was lost on Western strategists until Exocet missiles threatened British helicopter and Vertical and Short Take Off

and Landing (VSTOL) carriers in the South Atlantic during the Falklands War of 1982. But even the one or two Royal Navy submarines patrolling the area were sufficient to send scurrying the one Argentinian aircraft carrier. Lessons were readily available on both sides.

Britain's last fixed-wing flat-top, HMS *Ark Royal*, was retired in 1978 and only the existence of HMS *Invincible*, an anti-submarine warfare (ASW) cruiser, and HMS *Hermes*, both of which operated VSTOL Harriers, made possible a military campaign to retake the Falklands. Now, although *Hermes* will retire by the mid-1980s, all three Invincible-class carriers will be retained.

The Falklands War has also confirmed US

naval strategy since the early 1950s. Conflicts such as the Korean War (1950-53) and general deepening of the Cold War with the USSR stimulated new designs for large US naval forces. The first of a new class of carriers, USS *Forrestal*, was commissioned in 1955. It has a displacement of 60,000 tonnes and a 300-metre flight deck. Four of this class were eventually built. With a new angled flight deck, four lifts external to the hull, and four steam catapults, the Forrestal class set the trend in carrier design.

Kitty Hawk class

As an improvement on the Forrestal class, four Kitty Hawk-class carriers were built, the last of which was completed in 1968. These have re-located lifts to improve

Suggestions that large aircraft carriers, laden with aircraft, aviation fuel, ammunition and thousands of personnel, are as vulnerable as sitting ducks have been disproven by experience in actual combat. The secret of the carrier's success lies in the way in which it is protected, and there is every reason to believe that the USA and her allies understand its role in the defence of battle fleets and the projection of force to regions of hostility. The USA's *Nimitz* (far left), **Soviet** *Kiev* (above) and **British** *Hermes* (left) each have their own defences.

flight deck efficiency, a removed island farther aft and a defensive system based wholly on missiles.

The most significant step since the first of the Forrestal class was the laying down in 1958 of USS *Enterprise,* the world's first nuclear-powered carrier and second in the fleet to the atomic cruiser USS *Long Beach.* *Enterprise* carries eight nuclear reactors, in addition to four sets of Westinghouse steam turbines as used in the Forrestal and Kitty Hawk carriers. The flight deck is 336 metres long and 77 metres wide, and the displacement when laden is more than 91,000 tonnes. Carrying 50 per cent more aviation fuel than the Forrestals, *Enterprise* carries about 90 aircraft and more than 5500 personnel.

Fleet defence for US carrier battle groups is based on a triple-zone counter to conventional and nuclear attack. This strategy distinguishes an outer zone, an inner zone and a 'point' zone – the immediate vicinity of the carrier. The threat from intercontinental ballistic missiles (ICBMs) is minimal and perhaps non-existent. In the time it takes to send an ICBM from launch silo to target, the carrier would be more than 20 km away from its targeted location. Given that a specific set of targeting coordinates would necessarily be loaded in the ICBM at least 10 minutes before launch, the vulnerability is, in reality, even less.

Sea-skimming cruise missiles, favoured by the Soviets, or supersonic missiles launched by Soviet Backfire or Blackjack bombers would be countered first in the outer zone by combat aircraft from the carrier itself. On a typical flat-top of the Enterprise type, two squadrons of F-14 Tomcat interceptors would fly ranging missions far from the battle fleet. But thirsty fighters could not maintain 24-hr patrol or fly long distances with the anti-missile missiles (such as Phoenix) they would use against cruise weapons.

Sonar systems

If surprised, the carrier would be vulnerable in the outer zone. To match underwater threats (probably the most effective) battle groups rely on patrolling submarines and sonar systems to warn of an approaching enemy. Sophisticated ASW sensors, sonars dipped from helicopters and sustained activity by the carrier's own helicopter squadrons help to defer but not eliminate the threat.

The carrier's outer defensive zone would get little support from short-range helicopters, but other threats prevail closer in. Penetrating fighters would be picked up by early-warning aircraft orbiting the battle

Probably the greatest threat to surface vessels comes from submarines. Britain's *Invincible* (*left*) is an Anti-Submarine Warfare (ASW) cruiser which also operates VSTOL Harriers (*below*). Aided by its own helicopter squadrons, it employs sophisticated sensors, such as a dipping sonar (*below left*) to detect the enemy, but this merely lessens rather than eliminates the threat. The superiority of the USA's *Enterprise* and Nimitz-class carriers comes partly from the wide range of aircraft types they operate. These include SA-3 Vikings (*right*) for general defence, F-14 Tomcats (*below right*) for long-range strikes and E-2C Hawkeyes for early warning.

fleet, and SA-3 Viking, P-3 Orion and Light Airborne Multi-purpose System (LAMPS) helicopters would seek sneak attackers. Equipped with the Aegis Surface to Air Missile (SAM) system, destroyers would employ phased-array radar to automatically locate and track fast-moving targets traversing the middle zone.

Missiles and aircraft that get through to the inner zone would come under electronic, computer-controlled countersystems presenting a barrage of chaff, electronic countermeasures (ECMs) and rapid action guns, such as the 20-mm Phalanx built to stop a missile in flight with a devastating screen of depleted uranium-cored lead – pumping shells at 3000 rounds per minute. Confronted by the Close-In Weapon System (CIWS), very little would stand any chance of getting through. Decoys, SAMs, guns and ECMs all play their part in the rapid processing of target location, identification and elimination.

Point defence is considered a last-ditch attempt to save the carrier, but because escorts might in turn be exposed to devastating fire power from enemy ships and cruise missiles, the safety of the carrier might rest on its own systems.

Fuel to spare

In addition to the eight conventional carriers and the *Enterprise,* the US Navy operates three Nimitz-class carriers, making a total force of 12 Carriers. This inventory supports the world's third largest air force, in which there are 1200 aircraft afloat and 800 on shore. With eight nuclear reactors, the *Enterprise* steamed 383,000 km in three years before refuelling. The Nimitz class, first laid down in 1968, carries two reactors delivering the same power but with 13 years between refuellings. Each of the three carriers displaces 92,860 tonnes laden and has a deck 333 metres long, a complement of 6100 men, more than 90 aircraft capable of being catapulted into the air at three per minute, and three Sea Sparrow missile systems.

The Soviets recognize the asset held by carrier-equipped navies but, probably due to their own naval battle tactics, tend to regard them as expensively wasteful in war. Unlike US submarine fleets, which tend to

operate 'lone-wolf' patrols until on-board sensors detect suitable targets, Soviet submarines work in packs, steered to attractive targets by satellites or other Soviet ships. The Soviets, however, have shown determination to build a blue-water navy from what was, until the late 1960s, essentially a coastal defence force.

Although preceded by a Moskva-class helicopter carrier, the USSR's first flat-top was the *Kiev* VSTOL cruiser, displacing 38,000 tonnes laden, with a deck length of 274 metres. Its defences include missiles, ASW and anti-aircraft weapons and a complement of 15 Yak-36MP Forger Short Take-Off Vertical Landing (STOVL) aircraft. Each of the four Kiev-class vessels built by the early 1980s carried extensive ECMs, 13

radars and a large variable-dipping sonar. The Forger is an air defence fighter just capable of high-altitude supersonic flight, and has a limited (370 km) strike radius.

Limited performance

The Forger is not comparable with the Harrier, and appears to have both limited performance and restricted value, being of use only to fend off local air hostility or to attack shipping. Also, by contrast with the USA, the Soviets were late introducing their first nuclear-powered surface ship, although pride of place in that category went to the 23,000-tonne Kirov-class cruiser in 1980.

Yet for all their reluctance to build a large, fixed-wing, rolling-launched aircraft carrier,

the Soviets have been faced with the devastating firepower of large US vessels. In 1980, the Nimitz spent 108 days in the Arabian Sea when Soviet forces invaded Afghanistan. Many analysts believe the potential firepower presented by that carrier helped to check Soviet ambitions and underscore US intent to protect her oil resources in the Middle East.

Despite the massive costs of building, equipping and running aircraft carriers — even comparatively small ones such as *Invincible* — carriers are coming back into favour because of their mobility, firepower and ability to hit targets on land, at sea or in the air.

LAND WAR

Since World War II, a minor revolution has occurred in the development of modern infantry and artillery weapons and the ammunition they are designed to fire. A rifle round or shell is no longer simply a heavy object with high-speed penetrating power, but a subtle piece of physical and chemical engineering designed to give maximum destructive ability with maximum efficiency

The British Scimitar armoured reconnaissance vehicle exemplifies a modern trend towards increased mobility on the conventional battlefield.

THE DEADLY DUET OF BINARY WEAPONS

East and West are investing in a new kind of warfare. Two harmless chemicals, mixed together, make a cocktail that kills on contact, instantly

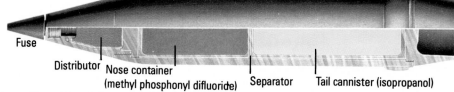

Fuse

Sarin (GB) nerve agent   Distributor

Fuse

Distributor   Nose container (methyl phosphonyl difluoride)   Separator   Tail cannister (isopropanol)

Above **The old and the new: the old chemical ammunition** *(top)* **contains the nerve agent in its lethal form – and is not immune to leaks. The binary shell** *(below)* **contains the two harmless components of GB. The separator keeps the two apart until the shell is fired – safely distanced from the soldiers dispatching it.**

Now in preparation for future warfare are chemicals so deadly that they can kill if a drop the size of a pin head settles on your skin. These so-called nerve gases have been in existence since before World War II, but they have been given a new potency by the introduction of devices known as binary weapons.

Binary weapons consist of two containers in which are two separate chemicals. Isolated from one another, they are as harmless in some cases as common salt. Mixed, they become nerve gas, blood agents or vesicants. All can kill or disable within a few seconds.

Pre-delivery, binary agents are safer than the gas shells, chemical bombs or rockets that they are replacing. In such projectiles the agent is stored in a container and spread by an explosive charge either as it approaches the target or when the shell hits the ground. In all of these systems there is the slight danger of an accident before the weapon is fired – while it is in transit or storage. There is also occasionally the danger of seepage through the walls of the projectile. In a binary weapon the agents are mixed only when the shell is in flight – this can be actuated by a time delay, by a radar signal which fires an explosive charge within the body of the shell or by air pressure.

Aerosol sprays

Binary systems can also be fitted to aircraft to be sprayed as an aerosol. The two chemicals are housed in separate tanks and the aircraft makes a fast, low pass over a target area. The major advantage of this system is that it puts a greater concentration of the agent into the target area in a shorter time than shells or rockets.

The binary system has an added advantage when the chemicals become due for disposal. Instead of having to dispose of a single highly toxic poison, the two separate sections of a binary system can be buried or dumped at sea with less risk of dangerous pollution.

Above **Today's battlefield weapons include the US M256 detector kit which can detect and identify chemical agents in time for counter-measures to be taken.**

Above **Dressed to kill – chemical warfare is a double-edged sword which requires a whole range of sophisticated defence equipment from respirators to activated**

carbon personal decontamination kits and hermetically sealed field hospitals. In a chemical war, a single drop of nerve poison on unprotected skin is all it takes.

Left **NBC (nuclear, biological and chemical) training is a priority in most armed forces. Binary weapons promise to make the lessons learned even more important to survival.**

Binary weapons are also easier to protect in peace time. To exploit their lethality, a terrorist group would not only have to secure both components, but they would also need to know how to mix them.

Though binary weapons are 'safer', there is a sinister suggestion that they could be used to deliver more lethal agents than have previously been considered safe for operational use. If the agent only becomes effective in flight, chemicals too deadly for normal systems could be used since they would become dangerous only in the planned target area.

Even now the existing agents are dangerous enough. The nerve gases attack a chemical in the body called cholinesterase. This enzyme controls the muscles by breaking down acetylcholine, the chemical which causes muscular contraction. In the absence of acetylcholine the body goes into spasms and the victim dies from asphyxiation. To add to their effect, nerve gases are colourless and odourless and so undetectable.

The nerve agent that has been used by the West since the Allies discovered and took over German stocks in 1945 is GB (Sarin). The USSR uses two other German agents, GA (Tabun) and GD (Soman). However, British and US scientists have developed a new nerve agent – the V agent— and the Americans refined this to produce VX which, with its oily texture, is highly persistent and lethal in doses of less than half a milligram.

The distinction between persistent and non-persistent agents is important since the latter will evaporate in a short time and can be used on the battlefield to support quick tactical thrusts, while the former will render whole areas unusable for days.

The future of chemical weapons is closely linked with genetic developments and there are suggestions that agents could be developed which would attack certain ethnic groups, since they would be the only people with the correct genetic characteristics to be vulnerable on the battlefield. Black women, for example, would lack the chromosomes which make most NATO soldiers vulnerable to the weapon. In a frightening scenario the genetically tailored device could be employed covertly by one nation against another to attack a whole male generation and destroy that nation's social system.

Explosive liquid

A crude but effective type of binary weapon is already available – the Fuel Air Explosive. This is an aerosol of explosive liquid which can be sprayed over a target area and then ignited by a shell or rocket. It is particularly effective in woods, jungles or hilly ground where enemy soldiers and tanks are likely to be massed for an attack.

Binary weapons are safer in peacetime, since they reduce the danger of accidents and misuse, but they could be a tactical disaster in war. The artillery battery or airfield which is waiting for the second chemical to be delivered could wait in vain if the stocks or transport system have been sabotaged or destroyed by the enemy.

Perhaps the greatest danger of binary weapons, however, is that they fall into a grey area in arms limitation talks. Nuclear and chemical warheads can be counted physically and their numbers and deployment agreed by treaty: not so binary weapons which consist, in their simplest form, of two piles of innocuous chemicals some distance apart. Unless binary weapons become the subject of a special treaty aimed at limiting the production of the two chemical agents, there is very little that can be done to prevent an horrific proliferation of these deadly killers.

TOYS FOR REAL SOLDIERS

Weapons simulators reduce the cost of living for those armies which use the most modern and expensive equipment

Warfare is both an art and a science. It takes practice to be good. But practice is expensive: a Euromissile MILAN anti-tank rocket costs about $20,000 a time. The soldiers who may have to use it for real will have only fired it about five or six times. Tanks are the same – at $2 million each they are too expensive to be used often in training.

So simulation is the name of the war game. A simulator is exactly what its name implies: it is designed to give the trainee all the signals and sensations he would normally expect if he were using the real thing in action. He can build up the all-important experience without using up millions of dollars-worth of ammunition.

Weapons simulators

Weapons like MILAN are catered for by simulators like the DX-143 or SIMLAN, both built in the UK by Dorand Electronics and Weston Simfire. Both systems fit a standard MILAN firing post, with their electronics housed in one of the two missile tubes normally carried by the gunner's number two. With the power supply in the second missile tube the crew have an apparently standard weapon.

The DX-143 simulator fits onto the MILAN sight unit: in front of the sight goes an optical unit containing a semi-transparent mirror at 45° to the sight lens. A spot of light simulating the tail-fire of the missile is projected onto the mirror when the firing button is pressed, and performs just like the real thing. In the case of MILAN, the missile appears in the sight from the right-hand side, and slightly below the cross hairs. Once the missile is 'acquired' by the controlling electronics all the operator has to do is keep the cross hairs on the target, and the missile flies towards it, the tailfire fading as it moves away. So it is with the simulator: the trainee then tracks a 'target' – anything from a car on a nearby road to a jogger – while the instructor watches through another sight unit to monitor his accuracy.

The smoke and dust of battle is simulated by an opaque glass shield which flips over the mirror, all but obscuring the tailfire. When the 'missile' reaches a pre-set range it 'explodes' by flaring up briefly and then dying.

Another facility on this simulator is the target. This is a moving square which is projected onto the mirror and which the trainee follows with the cross-hairs of his sight. The instructor can vary the 'speed' and 'direction' of its movement and the degree of accuracy required to achieve a good firing, which is shown in a digital readout.

The illusion of reality is made complete by slight variations between the performance of each 'missile' during flight – again like the real thing – and earphones which simulate exactly the sound of the missile going off and striking the target.

The great advantage of this particular simulator is that it is totally realistic and can be used in the field – in rain, mud, snow and high winds, all the conditions in which soldiers find themselves.

Tank crews have to stay alive as well, however. Crews have to learn the tactical skills of firing and manoeuvring, the skills which might keep them alive. They use a tactical simulator like the DX-175, another Dorand product, or the Weston Simfire SIMFICS.

Both are laser-based simulators consisting of a laser transmitter aligned with the tank's barrel, and a series of detectors on the

Above **Kill or be killed: at $20,000 a shot, MILAN is an expensive weapon on which to learn survival skills. Weston Simfire's SIMLAN helps to reduce the cost of living.**

turret. When the gunner draws a bead on a target the electronics and the laser transmitter assess which part of the tank the shell would hit and how much damage it would cause. If the shell missed, the attacker learns how and why at the subsequent de-brief; if the target is destroyed, however, its detector's electronics set off a smoke canister and switch off the engine.

These simulators can be extended to include a wide variety of weapons and be fitted to things like helicopters and MILAN. The detector's electronics are capable of working out what sort of fire is coming the target's way – small arms, missile, tank gun – and what (if any) damage it will cause. After the exercise all the data from attacker and target can be played back and a full classroom session worked on what went wrong and why.

SIMFIRE

Left **SIMFIRE is an anti-tank warfare simulator. When the gunner opens fire (*far left*) the target picks up the gun's laser pulse and makes contact with the attacker. Between them the two vehicles establish whether or not the target was hit (*centre*). In the event of a 'miss', the gunner fires again. If the target is hit this time (*left and right*) it emits smoke and the SIMFIRE control unit turns off the target's engine.**

Left and *above* SAWES allows the infantry to practise their fieldcraft and marksmanship under realistic conditions. A laser pulse from a rifle is picked up by the harness on the target's head and shoulders, setting off a buzzer. Umpires (*below*) can judge the result and reactivate 'dead' soldiers.

At a different level altogether is the Centronic Small Arms Weapons' Effects Simulator (SAWES) system. SAWES is designed to help teach individual infantrymen the basic skills of combat. It consists of a laser projector that is fitted to his rifle or machine gun and a receiver harness worn by each participant.

The receiver consists of 12 microprocessor-controlled laser detectors mounted on the head, chest and arms. A hit produces a loud buzz which the soldier can only silence by lying on his back.

An umpire gun can be used to test the receiving equipment, register a hit, or reactivate a 'dead' harness. Like the tank system, this equipment makes training vastly more realistic.

Right Smaller anti-tank weapons can be catered for as well. This unit can be programmed to simulate various types of weapon. It can be interfaced with the electronic SIMFICS equipment (*below*) fitted to tanks with computer-controlled sighting.

THE ULTIMATE RIFLE

It's every soldier's dream. It's light, accurate, quick-firing, and a real man-stopper. It may look like a toy, but don't be fooled. It's lethal.

It is not easy to take seriously – it seems to be made entirely out of plastic – and the bullets it fires are smaller than air rifle slugs. The bullets don't even have cartridge cases. But this is no child's toy. The Heckler & Koch G11 rifle is deadly. Bullets leave the barrel at 930 m/sec – and in such quick succession that the third has left the barrel before the recoil of the first is felt. If your enemy is within 600 m they'll go right through his steel helmet. The rifle and ammunition are so light that you can carry six times as many bullets as an enemy using a typical NATO 7.62 mm rifle. And every time you pull the trigger you've a 90 per cent better chance of hitting your enemy than he has of hitting you.

The West German Army, the Bundeswehr, is to adopt this rifle. The reasons behind the choice make an interesting illustration of how battle tactics and logistics can influence weapon design.

In the late 1960s the Bundeswehr began thinking about their next generation of small arms, and in a remarkable burst of openmindedness circulated manufacturers with an unusual invitation. Provided the weapon met the standard requirements regarding range, reliability and accuracy they would be prepared to accept any design however outlandish, on condition that it would guarantee to put a three-shot burst inside a circle no more than 1.2 to 2 mils in diameter. Since one mil is one-thousandth of any given range, this meant that the three shots had to fall within a 55 cm circle at 500 metres range.

This sort of accuracy is impossible with a conventional type of rifle or machine gun, because the recoil force after each shot lifts the barrel and disturbs the aim, so that successive shots are spread around. If a gun could be developed to fire at, say 2,500 rounds a minute, then it might be possible, since the three shots would follow each other very closely, before the recoil had

MECHANISM RECOIL

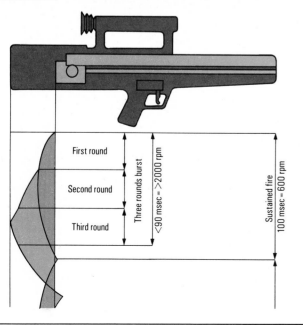

First round

Second round

Third round

Three rounds burst <90 msec = >2000 rpm

Sustained fire 100 msec = 600 rpm

OPERATING PRINCIPLE

▼ Feed direction

Cylinder in feed and ejection position

▼ Ejection direction

Cylinder in firing position

Firing pin

Barrel

Above **A radical departure from usual practice, the G11 is a new generation of weapon.** *Above right* **The burst fire capability gives a wide spread of bullets and a better chance of hitting the target. Its mechanism** (*left*) **is a closely guarded secret, but the principle of operation is disarmingly simple: the rotating bolt moves far faster than any ordinary rifle bolt could do, loading and firing three rounds in 0.075 secs.** *Far left* **Its stability depends on the long recoil stroke while firing bursts, single shots and on auto.**

moved the barrel very much. But the mechanical problems were excessive, and anyway, nobody wants a weapon which regularly fires at such a speed.

Heckler & Koch, the German weapon manufacturers, came to the conclusion that demand required a rifle with a gentle recoil (so as not to throw it off target), a flat trajectory and high velocity (to cut down the time of flight of the bullet), and a rate of fire in excess of 2,000 rounds per minute for the three-round burst. All this demanded a totally new approach to the mechanism. The first major decision was to adopt a caseless cartridge, a round of ammunition which dispensed with the conventional brass or steel cartridge case. This would lighten the soldier's load, and it would also simplify the design of the weapon since it would no longer have to mechanically extract and eject the empty case after each shot. Heckler & Koch collaborated with Dynamit Nobel, a firm with generations of experience in ammunition design, to develop a caseless round with a 4.7 mm bullet. This bullet is embedded in a solid block of propellant explosive, a percussion cap being embedded in the other end.

Small but deadly

The 4.7 mm G11 round is smaller than any bullet ever adopted for military service before, but it is extremely accurate, leaves the muzzle at 930 m/sec and can penetrate a standard German steel helmet at a range of 600 metres. It has a very flat trajectory, rising no more that 17 cm above the sight line when firing at 300 m range, so that there is no need to alter the sights for normal fighting ranges.

Having got the caseless cartridge, the next problem was to design a rifle to fire it. It was soon apparent that conventional rifle mechanisms were simply not suitable and that something totally new would have to be devised.

The full details of the mechanism are still secret, but enough has been revealed to permit an understanding of the basic principle of operation. The heart of the weapon is an unusual rotating breech-block which contains the firing chamber. This is a metal drum, bored to accept the cartridge, which rotates behind the rifle barrel. In the firing position the chamber is in line with the barrel: to re-load, the drum turns through 90° so that the chamber is vertical and a fresh cartridge can drop in from the magazine above.

When firing, the breech is rotated by the action of a gas-operated piston, tapping propellant gas from the barrel. There is a conventional firing pin behind the breech, which is operated by the trigger in the normal way.

The entire mechanism — barrel, breech, magazine, gas system and all — is concealed inside a futuristic reinforced plastic housing. This is shaped to form the butt and pistol grip and also to form a carrying handle which conceals an optical sight. The magazine, a long box containing fifty cartridges, is inserted horizontally above the barrel, so that the cartridges feed downwards into the breech. Except for the muzzle, there are no apertures which will allow water or dust to enter the weapon, the trigger and magazine being sealed by rubber flanges. The sight is provided with battery-illuminated cross wires for firing in poor light.

On firing, the entire mechanism, including the magazine, recoils inside the plastic housing against a spring buffer, so that the recoil felt by the firer is more in the nature of a gentle push than a sharp blow. The

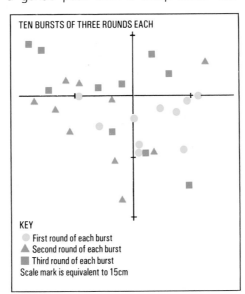

TEN BURSTS OF THREE ROUNDS EACH

KEY
● First round of each burst
▲ Second round of each burst
■ Third round of each burst
Scale mark is equivalent to 15cm

chamber revolves and is reloaded during the recoil movement and the rifle is ready to fire again immediately. A change lever above the trigger permits selection of either single shots, three-round bursts, continuous automatic fire, or a safe position. On changing to three-round bursts, the unique nature of this weapon becomes apparent.

The three shots are fired for a single pressure of the trigger, the noise of the shots blending into a single ragged report. As the first shot is fired, the mechanism of the rifle begins to recoil, and the trigger mechanism is disconnected: from now on firing is entirely controlled by the internal mechanism of the rifle.

During the recoil stroke the breech rotates and loads a second round, which is immediately fired and the recoil force of the second shot adds to the movement of the mechanism. Now the breech rotates again, reloads, and fires the third shot of the burst; once more the recoil force adds to the movement, and at last the mechanism is permitted to complete its rearward stroke, and return to the 'ready' position. The recoil movement within the plastic casing is, obviously, about three times as much as that of a single shot, but due to the buffering of the force felt by the firer is still relatively mild. The important thing is, however, that all three shots left the barrel *before* the firer felt the recoil shock and before the barrel began to move off target. Thus the three shots fly very close together and strike the target well within the designated spread.

What's the point? The point lies in the concept known as 'Hit Probability'. A single shot fired in combat by an average soldier has, perhaps, a 50% chance of hitting the target, depending on his marksmanship and factors like wind strength. Three shots, fired very rapidly and with a very small spread, improve the chance of hitting to something in the order of 95%.

Recoilless

When the G11 rifle is set to 'automatic' the mechanism works in a more conventional manner, making a recoil stroke for every shot fired and thus keeping the rate down to about 600-700 rounds per minute. Even with this rate of fire, the unique independent movement of the mechanism within its casing helps to absorb the recoil blow and the rifle has much less tendency to wander off target than does a conventional weapon in which the recoil force is felt more directly.

The logistic advantages of the G11 design show up when the weapon and its ammunition are compared to other standard weapons: for a given weight of 7.35 kg one can have the current standard German Army G3 rifle and 100 rounds of 7.62 mm NATO ammunition; or an American M16A1 (Armalite) with 344 rounds of 5.56 mm ammunition; or the G11 with 614 rounds of ammunition. At present the G11 weighs 4.26 kg and is made up of 155 component parts. The manufacturers intend to continue perfecting the design to bring the number of parts to 100 and the weight down to 3.6 kg – and make the rifle soldier-proof at the same time.

A standard load for most soldiers is about 400 rounds – 200 for himself, 200 for his squad's machine gun. That's 20 kg of 7.62 mm ammunition. He doesn't mind carrying the weight, the ammunition doesn't go far nowadays. If, for the same weight, he could carry six times as many bullets, he would be a happier man – and so would the people who must resupply him with ammo.

The development programme is scheduled to be completed in 1987: The Bundeswehr have committed themselves to adopting the G11 in 1990, a date arrived at purely on financial grounds and open to adjustment. But other NATO armies have expressed interest in the G11 and its ammunition, and it is not impossible that there could be co-production agreements and that the rifle could go into service with some other NATO army before 1990.

The concept of the caseless carriage is a tough pill to swallow for many conventionally minded experts. There are potential storage and safety hazards to be considered; there will be vast changes in national ammunition manufacturing capacity. But the weapon of tomorrow is here today, and rifle design will never be quite the same after this.

WHEN SHELL HITS TANK

What happens when irresistible force meets immovable object?

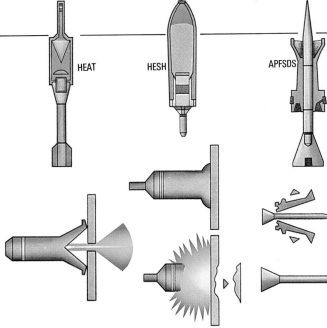

HEAT   HESH   APFSDS

Left The immovable object – the US Army's M-1 Abrams tank and (above far left) its 105 mm APFSDS ammunition. Nearly as effective is the 84 mm Carl Gustav, a recoilless rifle (above left and above) which fires a slower but deadly shaped-charge round. At close range the Carl Gustav is as effective as the tank.

A rocket from the American M72 rocket launcher weighs just 1 kilogramme. Less than half of that weight is explosive – but the rocket will still punch through 250 mm of armour plate at a range of 300 m. Yet tank designers claim that the new types of laminated armour they fit to their products will stop almost anything. If today's armourers claim their tanks are invulnerable while the weapon makers claim their products are unstoppable, where does the truth lie?

The simplest method of piercing armour is to throw something extremely hard at it extremely fast, so as to punch a hole in the plate. This used to be done with hardened steel shot, but as tank armour became thicker and tougher this approach failed because shot shattered on the outside of the tank. What was needed was a harder substance than steel, so tungsten alloys were adopted. Unfortunately these are much heavier than steel, and much more expensive. A shell made of tungsten weighs almost twice as much as a steel one and thus the gun would not be able to fire it fast enough to penetrate the tank.

The answer to this was to make a tungsten shot much smaller than the gun's calibre, surround it with light alloy to make a package that fitted the gun. When fired from the barrel the light alloy would fall away and leave only the tungsten to fly to the target. The combination of 'sub-calibre' tungsten shot and light alloy 'sabot' added up to a projectile weighing less than a plain steel shot, so that now the gun could fire it at the high velocities necessary for success.

A pin will burst a balloon more easily than a six-inch nail. In the same way, to achieve penetration we require the maximum mass of tungsten applied over the minimum area of the tank's armour. This means making the sub-calibre shot as long (for weight) and as slim as possible. But with a conventional rifled gun which spins the shot to keep it stable in flight, there is a limit to the length of shot which can be properly stabilised. So this line of reasoning brings us to today's anti-tank projectile, the APFSDS or Armour Piercing, Fin Stabilised, Discarding Sabot shot.

Fin-stabilised projectiles can be much longer than spin-stabilised types, and so today's sub-calibre shot is a long dart with fins at the rear end. It can be made of a tungsten alloy or, better still, of depleted uranium – uranium which is not radioactive in any way but which is even more dense and heavy than tungsten and therefore an even better penetrator.

Big guns

Propelled by a powerful cartridge, APFSDS rounds can attain velocities of over 1,225 metres per second, and due to their small cross-section and streamlined shape they lose very little of that speed during flight – about 18 m/sec per 1,000 metres – so that they strike the target with immense kinetic energy. A typical sub-projectile from a 120 mm APFSDS shot will hit a spot about 25 mm in diameter with the force of a 2-tonne car travelling at 10 m/s, and no steel can stand up to that. The shot pierces the tank, destroying the interior and splitting fragments of armour from the plating which compound the damage inside the vehicle.

The drawback to APFSDS ammunition is that it demands a heavy powerful gun from which to fire it; this is possible in a tank, which is big enough to carry such a gun, but not much good for foot soldiers. Heavy anti-tank guns were used during World War 2 but by the end of that war they were becoming too big to be handled on the battlefield and they have now been abandoned. Today, the 'man-size' anti-tank weapon relies principally upon explosive energy to defeat armour. Two methods are available, the 'squash-head' and the 'shaped charge' and of these the latter is most favoured.

The squash-head shell does exactly what its name implies; it consists of a shell full of explosive with a soft nose and a fuse in the rear end. Fired from a gun at relatively low velocities this shell deforms on striking the tank and deposits the plastic explosive on the outside of the armour in the form of a poultice, after which the fuse detonates it. The detonation sets up a shock wave inside the armour which travels through the plate and dislodges a large 'scab' from the inner surface. The scab is thrown off, into the tank, at high speed and becomes an extremely damaging missile; it ricochets inside the tank destroying crew and equipment.

To be effective, however, squash-head needs to be big – about 120 mm in calibre – though the gun need not be all that powerful since the round is slow in flight. But a big gun is still heavy and clumsy so squash-head is infrequently used: the shaped charge has almost completely replaced it.

The shaped charge is an explosive warhead with its forward face hollowed out into a cone, which is then lined with a thin metal liner. If the charge is now detonated from its rear end, away from the liner,

Left This sequence of photographs shows what happens when an 80 mm HEAT warhead hits 400 mm of armoured steel. A sensor in the nose of the warhead sets off the fuse while the main body of the explosive is some distance from the target. The detonation wave, set off at the correct distance, produces a jet of gas and molten metal which drills straight through the steel.

Above **The US Army's M 72A2 rocket launcher fires a tiny, but effective, 66 mm HEAT round.** *Above right* **To protect themselves, light tanks like the Scorpion rely on lightweight, heavily sloped, armour. But even this is not really proof against the uranium penetrator of an APFSDS round** (*right*).

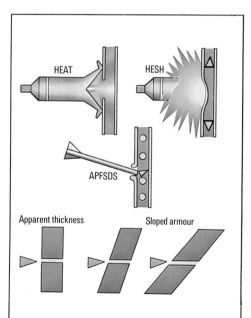

the effect of the detonation wave passing through the explosive is to deform the liner, subject it to immense pressure and heat, and turn it into a jet of molten metal and explosive gas moving at speeds in the region of 7-8,000 metres per second. When this jet strikes armour plate it simply forces a hole in the armour due to its combination of heat, mass and high velocity. The jet from a cone of 80 mm diameter is capable of piercing 3-400 mm of armour steel, delivering a blast effect inside the tank, together with fragments of armour blasted from the inner surface. The jet is also capable of igniting anything inside the tank which it strikes – fuel, ammunition, lubricating oil. A hit from a shaped charge is usually fatal.

The real asset of the shaped charge, however, is its size: an 80 mm shaped charge warhead fits snugly into a small, light missile which can be fired from a small, light rocket launcher or recoilless rifle. The shaped charge has revolutionised anti-tank warfare because it means that a single soldier holding what is basically a slim tube with a trigger on it can destroy 50 tonnes of tank.

But what is the tank designer's response to such weapons? Obviously a plain slab of steel is useless against full broadside attack by modern anti-tank weapons.

If you take a plate of, say, 100 mm thickness and tilt it at an angle, armour-piercing shot with a flat trajectory now has to penetrate much more than 100 mm. Tank designers take advantage of this, sloping their plates wherever possible to increase their apparent thickness. Moreover, a sloped plate is likely to cause the shot to skid off – or 'ricochet' – instead of piercing and in the case of long penetrators such as the APFSDS shot there's another advantage: the dense uranium and tungsten cores tend to be weak 'in shear' so that a violent sideways shock, caused by striking at an acute angle, may cause the core to snap, reducing the mass (and hence kinetic energy) by a considerable amount and thus reducing the striking force. So the first step

in protection is to slope – or 'ballistically shape' – the armour on the tank.

The second step is to subject the shot to disturbances during its penetration. If the armour is of even consistency the shot can pass through in one movement. But by using sheets of different material the shot can be checked and upset in its passage through the armour – perhaps well enough to prevent complete penetration. This is the function of laminated or 'Chobham' armour, a sandwich of steel and other substances which stress the shot as it tries to penetrate.

Chobham armour

The 'other substances' in the armour are not divulged, but it would be possible, for example, to put a layer of hard ceramic material between two sheets of steel. Another example of this sort of technique is in the incorporation of hard steel rods into the aluminium armour of troop carriers; the shot pierces the aluminium quite easily, but is suddenly deflected and checked by the steel rod and this is often sufficient to cause it to twist off-course, shear, and fail to pierce.

Laminated armour would quite easily defeat squash-head, since this type of round relies on a homogeneous armour plate in which to allow the shock wave to move; interrupting the wave by putting a different material in will disperse it and prevent damage being done to the inner surface.

Shaped charge is the most difficult weapon to stop, and types of laminated armour are now being examined in which chemical substances are trapped inside the lamination to drain off the heat of the jet and to 'smother' it in a layer of soft dispersed material. If you can reduce the jet's temperature, you have dispersed much of its energy. Kevlar armour, used successfully in 'bullet proof vests' could be usefully included in the lamination for this purpose.

At the present time, the ammunition designers are on top in the see-saw swing. Modern shaped-charge warheads can

penetrate any tank in existence and can go through as much as half a metre of armour – and no tank can carry so much steel. Ballistic shaping and laminated plate is doing much to protect against kinetic energy missiles, but there is much more work to be done before tanks can be considered proof against shaped charges.

And there is, maybe, something ironic in the fact that the wonder-fabric Kevlar is being utilized to protect both the soft human body and the rugged metal of the latest tanks against the onslaught of today's missile technology.

Above **Laminated armour relies on layers of a hard ceramic or nylon to disperse the energy of a HEAT round (A) and the shock wave from a HESH round (B). Hardened steel rods may cause APFSDS rounds to shear and fail to penetrate (C), while ballistically shaped – sloped – armour is 'thicker' (D) and deflects APFSDS penetrators.**

WHERE WISE MEN FEAR TO TREAD

A well-laid minefield can be an important first-line defence, but eventually the job of clearing it must be tackled

The detection and clearance of mines, like most areas of military technology, has seen many advances – advances which have been countered by new developments intended specifically to reduce or nullify their effectiveness. The battle between the mine layer and the mine lifter continues gingerly.

The first problem for a mine lifter is to determine the size of the minefield. Next he must identify the types of mines laid and then decide how he will set about clearing them. But rather than clearing all the mines, it is usually more important to breach the field, so troops and vehicles can pass through to attack the enemy on the far side. Usually, this procedure must be carried out swiftly and in secret, to maintain the element of surprise.

The tactics for clearing mines depend on the type of mines and how they were laid. In fact, a mine lifter must be knowledgeable about mine laying. Basically, there are two types of mines – anti-personnel (AP) and anti-tank (AT). Some AP mines contain sufficient explosive to cripple anyone stepping on them. Others spring out of the ground to explode, spreading shrapnel to kill or wound. A variation of this type is the *directional mine* (like the Claymore), which explodes sending ball bearings or steel rods

in a predetermined arc. These can be fired by remote control, or by a trip wire.

AT mines have a larger amount of explosive and are designed to cut a tank track, or wreck a vehicle such as a truck or jeep. Some mines combine the dual modes of AT and AP. These have a trip or pressure fuse, which sets off the explosion when trodden or kicked.

Minefields can contain either AP or AT mines, but for greatest effect and to make lifting more difficult a combination in various proportions of both types is usual. An additional hazard for engineers examining a minefield or clearing mines is the anti-handling device. This is a mechanism, fitted normally to AT mines, which detonates the mine if its removal is attempted. Some are built into the mines, but others must be

Right **An expert walks into a minefield carrying a detector. He is protected on lightweight, inflated platforms, which reduce the pressure of his footsteps below that required to detonate an anti-personnel mine.**

Left **Following the principle that machines work faster than men, tanks have been fitted with various devices to clear paths through minefields for other vehicles. A dual plough, working in front of the tracks, digs into the soil and pushes it to the sides of each track. Any buried mines are pushed aside or brought to the surface and exploded, but the system is not fool-proof. Some mines are designed to detonate at the least hint of being disturbed, and can trigger others.**

placed under or by the mine when it is laid.

Sometimes the only evidence of a minefield is the fencing and markings that some armies erect round the minefield to prevent civilians from wandering into the mined area, to deter the enemy and to warn friendly troops. Often, however, fencing and markings have been destroyed.

The most effective but time-consuming way to clear mines is to use a prodder. To do this, a sapper or assault pioneer crawls forwards, feeling the ground lightly with the hand and then probing with a long spike at an angle of about 45 degrees. When the spike contacts something hard, the searcher digs with the hands to clear the turf and expose the mine. The advantage of this method is that it can detect all types of mine.

A metal detector, which works by magnetism, was good for detecting older types of mines, but some modern mines are made of materials such as plastic, which cannot be detected other than by a prodder. A plastic mine has only a few small metal parts (a firing pin, or a percussion cap) which can be located only with extremely sensitive detectors. But these will also detect the metal junk scattered over any battlefield, so they can actually impede the task of mine detection.

Non-detectable mines can be hazardous to enemy as well as friendly troops. Some armed forces attack metal detector plates or rings to plastic mines, but retain the option to remove these before laying the mines. Although the detector plates make detection easier for the enemy, they also aid friendly troops in clearing their own mines.

Another aid to mine clearance is the *influence detector*, which in effect takes an X-ray of the soil and stores the information electronically. When a reading that varies from that in the memory is detected, the system raises an alarm. One disadvantage is that it will also react to large stones and other buried objects.

Sniffer dogs

An interesting system, used in World War 2 and Korea and revived for clearance in the Falklands, is the use of dogs. Training is based on association with rewards when a buried metal object is detected. Gun dogs, such as Labradors or Labrador cross-breeds, are most suitable, but spaniels are the most effective in waterlogged soils.

In three months, a dog can become an efficient mine sniffer. It can work quickly along roads, where individual mines have been laid with no apparent pattern, and can clear 30 metres a minute on a 2 metre wide path through a minefield. But even dogs have their limitations. Among these are the distractions of battle and people, as well as frozen or moist ground, long grass and heavily fought-over terrain.

Moreover, dogs have to be acquainted with one handler, and the affection that many handlers feel for the animals has to be restrained because too much attention ruins the dogs' training.

Once a mine is detected it can be attached to a long cable and pulled from a safe distance, but there are quicker ways of breaching a minefield. One method is to fire a hose filled with explosives across the field, then detonate the charge. The explosion will expose or destroy the mines along the path of the hose.

The equipment consists of a rocket attached to one end of several lengths of hose, which are linked together. At the other end is a parachute which deploys when the hose is fully extended, causing it to drop in a straight line across the minefield.

The system has been designed in two forms: a small man-packable version that blows a path about 1 metre wide suitable for infantry, and a giant version which can clear a path for vehicles. Clearly, the operational requirements of this system are that the men and vehicles should be in a position to follow up fast after it has been used and before the enemy have time to cover

Background **Mine-field clearance is a coordinated activity requiring the expertise of many groups of operatives. The mines they unearth are varied and can be unpredictable. An anti-tank mine (***far left***) can pack either a charge sufficient to seriously damage a tank, or a smaller one to cause it to merely shed its track. An anti-personnel jumping mine (***left***) can be lethal to anyone tripping the wire 40 metres away.**

ANTI-TANK MINE

1 Pressure plate
2 Pressure membrane
3 Striker
4 Plastic case
5 Detonator
6 Explosive charge

ANTI-PERSONNEL JUMPING MINE

1 Fuse cap
2 Strikers
3 Mine fuse
4 Splinters
5 Ejection charge
6 Mine body
7 Arming wire
8 Explosive charge
9 Detonator

the exits with rifle fire.

On a smaller scale, the Bangalore torpedo – an explosive-filled tube – can be used to breach the border of a minefield. The advantage of the system is that it can be pushed discreetly under barbed wire, destroying it and any mines nearby.

The most dramatic explosive technique, however, is *fuel air explosive* (FAE). This employs a petroleum-based aerosol, which is introduced into the area by a low-flying aircraft, or a succession of artillery shells. When the air is saturated with the vapour it is detonated. The resulting explosion over a wide area can not only clear the vegetation, but expose and often detonate the mines laid below ground. However, as can be imagined, it needs still air and ideally a bowl-shaped or hollow terrain in which the FAE can collect. It is particularly effective in still woodland or jungle.

The mechanical methods of clearing mines are tested systems also dating from

World War 2. Tanks and other AFVs are fitted with either giant rollers on an articulated arm in front of the vehicle, or a drum fitted with chains which revolve and flail the ground ahead. As the vehicle advances, the chains detonate all the mines in their path, and so provide a route for other vehicles to follow. However, the simple way to counter this is to link one mine with no fuse to another which is fully armed. When one mine is detonated it also sets off the other one – which might be under the tracks of the tank.

Double action fuse

A more sophisticated mine can be fitted with a fuse which is operated by two separate actions. For example, the mine can be armed by a tank's rollers and set off by the track.

A simpler mine clearing device consists of a plough fitted to the front of a tank. This has a small blade that digs into the ground

just in front of the tracks, pushing the mines to one side as it advances, and it is a common device on Warsaw Pact tanks.

Counter-measures

There are two ways in which this can be countered. The first is an anti-disturbance fuse, which detonates the mine as soon as it is moved. The explosion might not harm the tank, but it will probably damage the plough blades. The other device is the tilt fuse, which is commonly fitted to traditional anti-tank mines of the circular plate design. It consists of a 60 cm long rod screwed into the centre of the mine, designed to explode the mine when the leading edge of the tank pushes it out of alignment. This defeats the many ploughs that are fitted only to clear in front of the individual tracks.

These mines require more time and patience when they are laid, so they are impractical as the only type in a large minefield. They will probably be placed on

Right **The alarm from a mine detector might be due to a harmless object, or, in the case of a plastic mine, there might not be an alarm. The sequence (*below*) begins with the location of a mine by prodding, and ends with the controlled detonation of it. To be successful, the operatives must cover every metre of ground, working in a pattern.**

ARMS RACE

Global strategies and maintenance of the military balance combine to produce an ever-growing arsenal of weapons many times greater than any one side could ever need to defeat the other. This threat alone – known as MAD, for Mutually Assured Destruction – precariously maintains a perilous peace

A Tomahawk ground-launched Cruise missile is test fired from its transporter during trials in the US.

THE ARMS RACE
Dr. Strangelove
meets MAD MaX

Right **These charts show the extent and state of readiness of the US nuclear might. Warheads can be delivered by any of three means – bomber aircraft, submarine-launched ballistic missiles (SLBMs) and inter-continental ballistic missiles (ICBMs). This triad force of delivery vehicles results partly from**

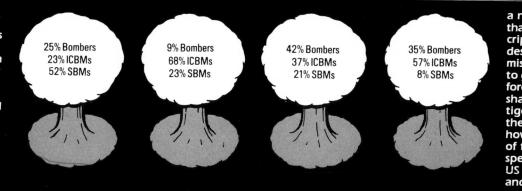

25% Bombers
23% ICBMs
52% SBMs

9% Bombers
68% ICBMs
23% SBMs

42% Bombers
37% ICBMs
21% SBMs

35% Bombers
57% ICBMs
8% SBMs

a need to ensure that no enemy could cripple the USA by destroying all its missiles, and partly to give the army, air force and navy equal shares in the pres-tige of defending the nation. Today, however, each limb of the triad has a specific function in US nuclear strategy, and their strength can vary.

The world today is stocked with sufficient nuclear armaments to virtually extinguish all life on Earth. Increasingly, people are concerned that a minor incident could trigger off a major nuclear war that would leave several hundred million dead and many millions more injured and dying. This capability for mass destruction did not arise from some uncompromising military plans for major conflict. It is, instead, the result of a succession of errors, both in judgement and planning, coupled with gross belligerence and a need for territorial control that goes back to the days of World War 2.

Mankind's last stand

The seeds of what could be Man's final conflict were sewn in the uncertain months after war's end in 1945. Denied almost all prospect of independent survival, countries occupied by Soviet forces (Poland, East Germany, Czechoslovakia, Hungary, Romania and Bulgaria) became a buffer zone against invasions into Soviet territory. Determined that central Europe would never again pose a threat, the Soviets pursued a dominating policy which prevented national independence and rapidly brought each East European country under the control of Moscow.

In the West, Britain, France and the USA assumed an opposite stance. Concerned for the economic welfare of Germany, they restored national government, free elections and, gradually, a level of independence to West Germany. And with old empires shaken aside by six years of world war, both the USA and the USSR acquired grand, international ambitions that fuelled the distrust each had for the other. In the USA, anti-communist feeling ran high. Moreover, with communist forces in control in China, the threat to the West was seen in simple terms – one-third of the world's people, the vast expanse of Eurasia from the Baltic to the China Sea, was under communist domination.

The military response to the communist threat was spurred by a most significant development in new weapons – the atom bomb. It provided, in a single charge, the explosive power of 40,000 conventional bombs. Such a yield is equivalent to the total load from 3500 wartime bombers dropped at the same time on a single target. Soon, the USA manufactured atomic bombs in large numbers – by 1950, she had more than 100, and a rapidly expanding force of strategic bombers – but US military supremacy on such a grand scale was not to last. In 1949, the

Soviets tested an atomic device, and Britain's first atomic test followed in 1952. Nevertheless, the USA had built up a formidable lead in what had become the most competitive arms race of all time. By 1955, the USA had nearly 2000 atomic weapons, compared with about 20 in the Soviet arsenal.

Exploiting the H-bomb

During the 1950s, with huge bombers like the B-36, a ten-engined aircraft capable of lifting a 30-tonne bomb load, the USA was suitably equipped to exploit the more lethal hydrogen bomb when it became available in 1952. Although the USSR was only a year behind tests with the H-bomb, they were again disadvantaged in the nuclear arms race by the superior production facilities available to the USA.

The step from atom bomb to H-bomb was most significant. The H-bomb, unlike an atomic bomb, was not limited to a specific explosive force, but could be sized as required. In theory, single-bombs could be built with an explosive yield equivalent to 5000 bombs the size of that dropped on Hiroshima. In practical terms, however, a 20 MT (megatonne) bomb, equivalent to 1000 times the size of the Hiroshima bomb, is adequate to destroy most targets.

Although the Hiroshima bomb had a yield 1740 times that of the largest conventional bomb dropped during the war, the development of the H-bomb increased the destructive capability of the super powers far greater than did the development of the atom bomb. This point was missed by popular observers who sought to group all nuclear weapons into the same category, but of even greater significance was that the massive increase in the destructive capability of a single H-bomb reduced greatly the size and weight of a device capable of completely destroying a major city. Seen against an atom bomb, then, the H-bomb is a small, lethal, lightweight weapon. Harnessed to long-range missiles, it provided a deterrence as good as if not better than any manned bomber.

To this end, the USA has expended heavily in Minuteman intercontinental ballistic missiles (ICBMs) based in underground concrete silos. Within six years of their deployment in 1961, ICBMs numbered 1000 – a force supplemented by 54 Titan missiles. Each Titan carried a single 9MT warhead, compared with a Minuteman's 1-2MT. Despite a formidable arsenal of fixed silo

Above **Preparing a mine for detonation can be almost as hazardous as mine detection. It must be unearthed carefully, and there can be no risk of failing to detonate it on the first attempt, because subsequent attempts could be fatal.**

the forward edge where enemy sappers with specialized AFVs are likely to start to breach the minefield. If they set off mines at this point, the men defended by the mines can then make the breaching even more difficult by engaging the enemy sappers with small arms and artillery fire.

Strategy

It is an important strategy that all obstacle systems — be they minefields, barbed wire, concrete, timber or steel road-blocks — should be defended. Without the capability to disrupt clearing operations by gunfire, the minefield becomes merely a nuisance.

Unlike other weapons, mines do not discern between friends and enemies, and the left-overs from World War 2 and other wars still present a hazard to soldiers and civilians. This is compounded by the movement of desert sand or sea-shore shingle. Any laying pattern that may have existed has been disrupted, while the mines can become more unstable as the explosive deteriorates and the mechanisms become rusty and unreliable. An anti-tank mine designed to explode under the weight of a heavy vehicle can, after 50 years, be set off by a wandering pedestrian or even explode spontaneously. Indeed, unpredictability is the mine clearer's greatest enemy.

The latest addition to the US submarine fleet is the Ohio class nuclear-powered submarine (*above left*), which packs 16 of the deadly accurate Trident missiles (*above, far right*). These replace the less accurate, but equally potent, Poseidon missile (*above centre*). Besides the 16 missile chamber lids, visible on top, the Ohio subs have little to distinguish them from previous classes.

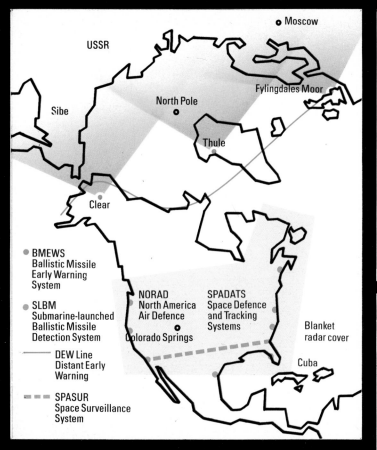

- **BMEWS** Ballistic Missile Early Warning System
- **SLBM** Submarine-launched Ballistic Missile Detection System
- **—— DEW Line** Distant Early Warning
- **- - - SPASUR** Space Surveillance System

USSR
Moscow
North Pole
Fylingdales Moor
Sibe
Thule
Clear
NORAD North America Air Defence
Colorado Springs
SPADATS Space Defence and Tracking Systems
Blanket radar cover
Cuba

Above **For a missile travelling at three times the speed of sound across the North Pole, only a few minutes' flying time separate the USA from the USSR. From a central command post, hidden deep within the Cheyenne Mountain in Colorado, the USA maintains constant vigil through a network of satellites, radar and radio antennae, intended to give early warning of attack from any direction. Based on reliable estimates of the US nuclear arsenal** (*right*), **there is widespread disagreement about the adequacy of the US deterrence. The bomber limb of the US forces is centred on the ageing B-52** (*far right*), **to be replaced by the lethal B-1** (*below*).

USA: ESTIMATED STRATEGIC NUCLEAR WARHEADS			
INTERCONTINENTAL BALLISTIC MISSILES (ICBM)			
SYSTEM	NUMBER DEPLOYED	WARHEADS PER LAUNCH VEHICLE	TOTAL WARHEADS
Minuteman 2	450	1	450
Minuteman 3	350	3	1050
Minuteman 3 Mk12A	200	3	600
Titan 2	52	1	52
SUBMARINE-LAUNCHED BALLISTIC MISSILES (SLBM)			
Poseidon C3	304	10	3040
Trident 1 C4	216	8	1728
SUBTOTALS ICBM/SLBM	1572		6920
AIRCRAFT			
B-52D	75	4 bombs	300
B-52G	151	4 bombs, 4 missiles	1208
B-52H	90	4 bombs, 4 missiles	720
TOTALS	1888		9148

USA: ESTIMATED TOTAL MEGATONNAGE			
INTERCONTINENTAL BALLISTIC MISSILES (ICBM)			
SYSTEM	TOTAL WARHEADS	MEGATONS PER WARHEAD	TOTAL MEGATONS
Minuteman 2	450	1.5	675
Minuteman 3	1050	0.17	179
Minuteman 3 Mk12A	600	0.34	204
Titan 2	52	9.0	468
SUBMARINE-LAUNCHED BALLISTIC MISSILES (SLBM)			
Poseidon C3	3040	0.04	122
Trident 1 C4	1728	0.1	173
SUBTOTALS ICBM/SLBM	6920		1821
AIRCRAFT			
B-52D	300	1.0	300
B-52G	1208	1.0/0.2	725
B-52H	720	1.0/0.2	432
TOTALS	9148		3278

ICBMs and manned, penetrating bombers, such as the B-45 and the B-52, US planners seized on a third line of deterrence – the submarine-launched ballistic missile (SLBM). This triad of forces (bombers-ICBMs-SLBMs) was established to prevent a single Soviet technological breakthrough from crippling the US strategic nuclear deterrent.

This represented the first shift away from the USA's immediate post-war nuclear strategy. Called Assured Ascendancy, it sought to deter communist aggression and to give the USA a war-winning capability. With massive forces capable of hitting any target in the Soviet Union, US policy was to be able to respond to communist initiatives by beating them into submission. That policy prevailed only so long as the Soviets were unable to strike back – and during the early 1960s, they acquired an expanding force of ICBMs and SLBMs to do just that.

By 1963, the Assured Ascendency philosophy was extinct. It was replaced by Assured Destruction, which carried with it the implicit capability of devastating Soviet economic, industrial and social infrastructures no matter what the USSR might do to the USA. Popularly termed the Mutually Assured Destruction (MAD) concept, this strategy ensured that even with forces the USA could not stop, and recognizing the enormous probable damage to US civilian targets, the Soviets could never cripple the USA's ability to devastate the USSR. In that way, read the philosophy, only a lunatic would start a war that would inevitably end in assured self-destruction.

The new concept was embraced as having one decisive advantage over the previous philosophy. Because neither side could effectively come out on top following a strategic nuclear war, each would find it advantageous to enter arms-control negotiations. Such negotiations began six years later. By 1967, the US nuclear deterrent was numerically frozen at 1054 ICBMs in underground silos and 656 SLBMs in 41 nuclear-powered submarines. The total 1710 strategic nuclear missiles and their warheads threatened almost all Soviet territory, whereas the USSR in that year had less than 600, most of those (460) in the form of land-based ICBMs. But the USA had several other options, including 588 B-52 nuclear bombers. Even before 1963, under the policy of Assured Ascendency, the Soviets failed to demonstrate a single penetrating bomber to threaten continental USA. Yet, even the nearly 500 or so nuclear-armed missiles fielded by the USSR had been sufficient to topple the concept of Assured

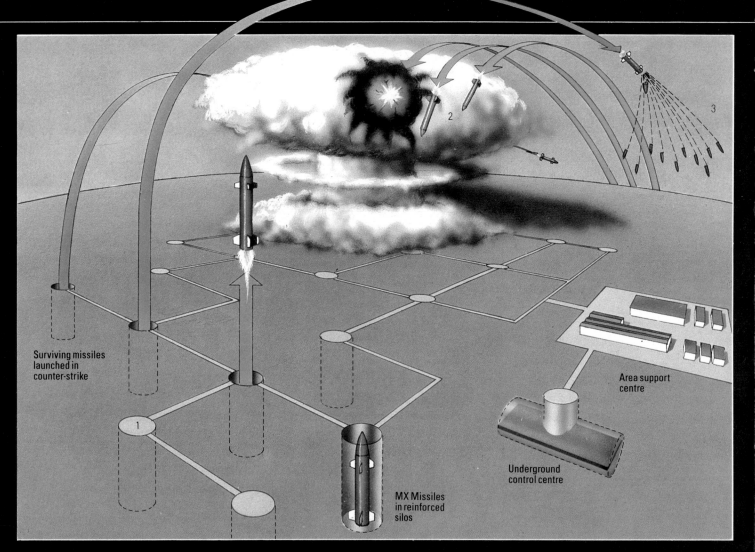

Surviving missiles
launched in
counter-strike

Area support
centre

Underground
control centre

MX Missiles
in reinforced
silos

Ascendency and invoke the Assured Destruction philosophy.

The Assured Destruction philosophy was short lived. A variation called Assured Anxiety emerged during the late 1960s. This called for a flexible response rather than an all-out retaliation. It was prompted when President Nixon debated whether the only option he had against a pre-emptive Soviet attack should remain one of slaughtering Soviet civilians – the only result being to invoke more US dead.

Civilians as hostages

An evolving school of thought on the flexible response concept believed that lower levels of defence would be effective only if both sides were deterred by fear of total annihilation. To maintain world peace, said the theorists, a threat of mutual vulnerability must prevail, making nuclear victory impossible and effectively holding hostage the several hundred millions of ordinary people on both sides. Towards that end, said the philosophy, any attempt to reduce the threat of mutual extinction would lessen the credibility of deterrence and make war more likely.

That was partly served in reality by an agreement to limit the number of anti-ICBM missiles capable of knocking out incoming warheads. If too many were deployed, the threat of mutual destruction would be lessened, but if a few were allowed around ICBM silos, effectively making them immune to attack, the concept would be enhanced due to the assured survivability of a retaliatory force. When the urgency to begin talks on nuclear weapons peaked late in the 1960s, the Soviets were rapidly closing the gap between the Soviet and US deterrent forces. Facing 1710 missiles, the USSR increased her inventory from less than 600 in 1967 to 1950 in 1971 by 1982, the Soviet inventory was around 2400, of which 39 SLBMs were outside the levels agreed at the Strategic Arms Limitation Talks (SALT).

Above **Dense Pack Formation was one of many methods of deployment considered for the US MX missile system. It consisted of 100 MXs underground (*1*) in a rectangular area so that each was 550 m from five neighbours. The theory was that enemy missiles needed to neutralize such a field would be blown up by the first blasts (*2*). leaving each surviving MX to counter with 10 warheads (*3*). Each MX warhead packs a blast equivalent to 1000 times that of a Hiroshima type bomb (*right*).**

The assessment of the relative strengths of the Soviet and US nulcear forces has been complicated by the introduction of missiles with multiple warheads. These are either *multiple re-entry vehicles* (MRVs), which all fall in more or less the same area when released by the missile carrying them, or *multiple independently targetable re-entry vehicles* (MIRVs), which are guided to separate targets after release from the missile. Because MRVs cannot be assigned to separate targets, they are often classified as single warheads. The SALT 2 Treaty, signed in 1979 but still not in force, makes no distinction between single warheads and MRVs, but limits the number of MIRVed missiles permitted.

The credibility of deterrence

In 1983, the US view was that a major programme of force modernization was long overdue and that new missiles were essential if the credibility of deterrence was to be maintained. In the firm belief that deterrence is the best way to stop all forms of strategic aggression, US defence policy is founded on the need to prevent war under any circumstances. These aims can be achieved, say the Americans, only if the Soviets continue to accept vulnerability in the interest of global peace – time will tell.

THE ARMS RACE
The Dialectics of Death

The endless spiral of threat and counter-threat promises to keep the nuclear arsenals of the super-powers well stocked.

The USSR and the USA are firm in their resolve not to start a nuclear war. Yet both are convinced that if a war starts, they will have to fight to the finish. Highly detailed studies show that without involving European countries, a total nuclear exchange between these two superpowers would result in 175 million US, 123 million Soviet and 17 million European deaths. A further 15 million would suffer genetic damage and about 5 million pregnant women would abort. Contrary to assertions from certain elements in Europe, the USA and the USSR, there can be no nuclear free zone, but the debate continues.

Some top Soviet military leaders believe nuclear war is justified, even though it may be the least desirable option. Balancing this view is the influence of political leaders in the Kremlin who are firm in their belief that in the event of a nuclear war, damage to the Soviet state would be total and that nuclear war should be avoided at any cost. They see the need for deterrence as paramount.

During the past 35 years, US concepts of nuclear deterrence have altered repeatedly as the number and diversity of nuclear weapons and the delivery systems (aircraft and missiles) have expanded.

By contrast, Soviet concepts follow a less circuitous route by simply asserting a need for supremacy. Soviet military strategy aims to suppress enemy forces rapidly before they could threaten Soviet territory. The

In a state of constant preparedness, a missile crew of the Soviet Air Defence Force exercises with one of the many missiles that guard the Soviet sky.

option to use intercontinental ballistic missiles (ICBMs) flying high above the land battle can be eliminated only if Soviet rocket-forces are stronger, or so hold the Kremlin strategists.

Seen from the West, this overwhelming capability goes beyond mere deterrence, and amounts instead to a threat of pre-emptive attack. At this point, deterrence becomes provocation. In fact, there is dispute about the point at which a force sufficient to prevent attack becomes large enough to provoke war.

Nevertheless, Soviet military strategy has for a long time been prepared for a nuclear war that could probably be survivable or even winnable. Such a war, they envisage, could result from a local conflict, but US observers think it more likely to result from a pre-emptive attack.

Soviet strategists strive for the survivability of the socialist state, shored up by a strong nuclear force. But should the state be devastated by a war, all is not lost because, they argue, the worker-society imperative for achieving socialist goals would

Below left **An impressive display of rockets forms part of the customary Soviet military parade – seen by the West as a centrepiece for advancing political ideology.**

Below **Made extremely sinister by its ease of concealment, a Soviet SS-1 Scud missile ambles through the undergrowth. It could be launched from its carrier in minutes.**

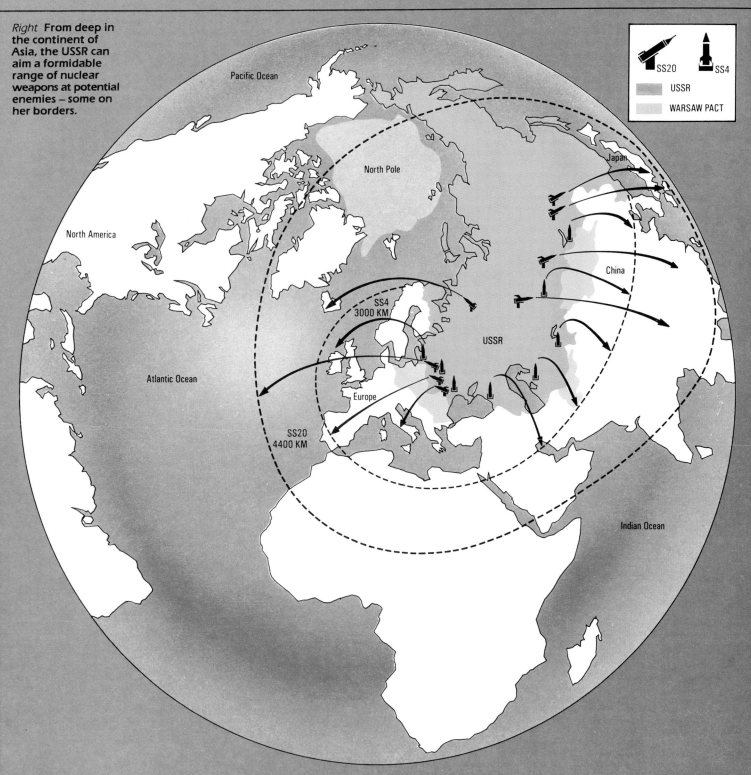

Pacific Ocean

North Pole

North America

SS4
3000 KM

USSR

Atlantic Ocean

Europe

SS20
4400 KM

Japan

China

Indian Ocean

SS20   SS4

USSR

WARSAW PACT

ultimately be restored – albeit at great length.

Accordingly, Soviet aims in the event of either nuclear or conventional war are not to waste military resources on punitive reprisals, but to first defeat opposing forces, prevent damage to the USSR, retain intact the functions necessary for rapid Soviet expansion, establish political control over the defeated enemy and convert the people to Soviet ideology. These strategies have already been observed in the countries of Eastern Europe, after the Soviet defeat of the Nazi forces in those countries in World War 2 between 1944 and 1945.

There is a popularly-held view, yet to be convincingly dispelled by the Pentagon, that by deploying weapons with a first-strike capability, the West is prepared to fight a winnable nuclear war. This notion is nurtured by the USSR to support another important element of Soviet nuclear policy – that Soviet defences are deployed reluctantly to protect a vulnerable Soviet Union from aggressive Western intentions. In fact, official delegates to arms reduction talks are convinced that it is in fact Soviet policy which avidly follows the concept of jus-

tified, winnable nuclear war.

When President Kennedy threatened the USSR over plans to site Soviet missiles in Cuba, it came as a surprise even to US strategists that the USA had 200 ICBMs and submarine-launched ballistic missiles (SLBMs) to fewer than 10 equivalent Soviet rockets.

From the humiliation of having to back down over the Cuban missile crisis the USSR set in motion an expansion of the Navy and came increasingly to accept the missile as a valuable asset.

By the end of the 1960s, the USSR had

USSR: ESTIMATED STRATEGIC NUCLEAR WARHEADS			
INTERCONTINENTAL BALLISTIC MISSILES (ICBM)			
SYSTEM	NUMBER DEPLOYED	WARHEADS PER LAUNCH VEHICLE	TOTAL WARHEADS
SS-11/SS-11MRV	230/290	1/3	1100
SS-13	60	1	60
SS-17	150	4	600
SS-18	308	8	2464
SS-19	360	6	2160
SUBMARINE-LAUNCHED BALLISTIC MISSILES (SLBM)			
SS-N-5	18	1	18
SS-N-6/SS-N-6MRV	102/272	1/3	918
SS-N-8	290	1	290
SS-NX-17	12	1	12
SS-N-18	256	3	768
SUBTOTALS ICBM/SLBM	2348		8390
AIRCRAFT			
Tu-95 Bear	100	3 bombs	300
Mya-4 Bison	56	2 bombs	112
TOTALS	2504		8802

USSR: ESTIMATED TOTAL MEGATONNAGE			
INTERCONTINENTAL BALLISTIC MISSILES (ICBM)			
SYSTEM	TOTAL WARHEADS	MEGATONS PER WARHEAD	TOTAL METATONS
SS-11/SS-11MRV	1100	1.0/0.2	404
SS-13	60	1.0	60
SS-17	600	0.5	300
SS-18	2464	0.625	1540
SS-19	2160	0.5	1080
SUBMARINE-LAUNCHED BALLISTIC MISSILES (SLBM)			
SS-N-5	18	1.0	18
SS-N-6/SS-N-6MRV	918	1.0/0.2	265
SS-N-8	290	1.0	290
SS-NX-17	12	1.0	12
SS-N-18	768	0.2	154
SUBTOTALS ICBM/SLBM	8390		4123
AIRCRAFT			
Tu-95 Bear	300	1.0	300
Mya-4 Bison	112	1.0	112
TOTALS	8802		4535

overtaken the USA in numbers of missiles deployed, but the Soviets interpreted technical improvements to US missiles as posing a greater threat than before.

From 1970, an increasing number of Minuteman ICBMs were fitted with three warheads, and the submarine-launched Poseidon missiles were each fitted with up to ten small warheads. So, although the number of missiles remained the same, the number of threatened targets, and the warheads to reach them, increased dramatically.

In 1977, the USA had 2154 warheads on 1054 ICBMs, and 5120 warheads on 656 SLBMs – a total of 7274 strategic warheads, compared with 1710 just ten years earlier. By 1977, the Soviets had 1500 land-based missiles and 989 submarine-launched missiles – a total force of nearly 2500 warheads. But the USSR, too, had started deploying more warheads on each missile and, beginning in 1976, quickly built up their warhead inventory, reaching a total 5600 by the end of the decade and over 8000 by the end of 1982.

Some adjustments are necessary to these totals, because the USA took out of commission some of the older submarines, reducing its strategic warhead inventory to about 6920, but retained more than 2000 nuclear bombs on strategic aircraft, bringing to over 9000 the total US warhead inventory. Added to the Soviet list are more than 400 nuclear bombs on aircraft capable of reaching the USA, giving a warhead total of about 8800.

On numerical balance, the USA has a slight advantage in strategic nuclear weapons, but the numbers can be made to fit several different arguments. If warheads instead of rockets are compared, the USSR has a slight numerical advantage, with

Left **A vast army of lethal Soviet tanks was one reason the USA prepared for a tactical nuclear war, but the Soviets see this escalating quickly to include their nuclear submarines** (*below*) **and Backfire bombers** (*below right*)**, both nuclear armed.**

more than 8000 warheads on missiles compared with the USA's 6920. Moreover, about 6380 Soviet warheads are on silo-based ICBMs facing 1052 US ICBM silos – a numerical advantage of over five to one. On the same basis, the USA's 2152 ICBM warheads face nearly 1400 Soviet ICBM silos – a ratio of only 1.5 to one.

Because only land-based missiles on either side have the accuracy to knock out opposing silos, and so gain a dramatic advantage from a pre-emptive strike, the Soviets are considered by the USA to have a dangerously destabilizing superiority, not in weapons or warheads but in the way a war could develop. However, following this argument, say the Soviets, if both sides used their inventories exclusively to knock out the enemy's silos, about 7150 nuclear warheads would remain on the US side with which to attack other military and industrial targets, whereas the USSR would have only 1800.

Not so, say US strategists, because the increasing accuracy of Soviet ICBM warheads, already observed in tests, would require the USSR to assign only two warheads to each of the 1052 US silos to be sure of destroying them. This leaves the USSR an additional 4200 highly accurate ICBM warheads to be targeted at super-hardened sites, such as command posts and underground control stations.

The Soviets counter this by pointing to the increasingly accurate US submarine-launched missiles – the Tridents. When Trident 2 comes fully into operation, it will have an accuracy at least as good as current US ICBM warheads, joining the land-based leg of the triad in threatening super-hardened silos and other sites. If no more than ten boats are built, the 24 missiles carried by each would add 2400 warheads to the US inventory. And to upgrade the US ICBM force, the MX missile is in development, with the capacity to carry ten warheads and the same explosive yield as the USSR's largest ICBM, the SS-18.

THE ARMS RACE
Europe – caught in the crossfire?

Left **A Boeing B-52 being refuelled in flight from a flying tanker. This and the next generation of nuclear-capable conventional bombers are given greatly increased range by refuelling in flight, and can operate well beyond the continental United States.**

The US Pershing 2 tactical nuclear missile, a development of the Pershing 1 and 1A, combines pinpoint accuracy with compactness and mobility. The missile and mobile launch trailer can be air-lifted to the war zone.

Since it was agreed to deploy US Cruise and Pershing 2 missiles in Europe, fears have increased that nuclear war is becoming more likely every year. Thoughts of indiscriminate mass death have aroused public revulsion for a defence strategy many see as immoral and potentially genocidal, and stimulated the rapid recent growth of the anti-nuclear campaigns in Britain and on the Continent. But although Europeans agree about the horror of nuclear war, not all are anti-nuclear. Perhaps the most forceful argument for a nuclear deterrence in Europe is that in the past, sudden changes in the balance of power have invariably led to war, so unilateral disarmament could bring about the very danger it seeks to prevent. The debate is likely to continue for many years, but how has it developed?

Historically, the Soviet Union fears Europe and believes the greatest threat to its survival comes from the combined forces of the North Atlantic Treaty Organization (NATO). The Soviets fought World War 2 expecting to be attacked by the eventual winner – the Allies or Germany. The Allies did not attack the USSR, but she has since looked with suspicion on the build-up of forces in Europe by NATO countries, which consistently reaffirm their intention to add to the defence forces of that region. Moreoever, the Soviets strongly deny that there are any justifiable US military interests in the area.

Just as the Warsaw Pact countries (the USSR, Poland, East Germany, Czechoslovakia, Hungary, Romania and Bulgaria) contribute military resources to the combined defence of the Eastern Bloc, so the NATO countries supply arms and troops to defend the West. Non-Soviet Warsaw Pact countries contribute 1.1 million troops, compared with 3.7 million from the USSR; added to these are 7.1 million Soviet and Warsaw Pact reservists.

NATO's manpower
Facing the 4.8 million Warsaw Pact troops are 3.2 million servicemen in Western Europe, including France. But more than 2 million US troops elsewhere, plus 900,000 reservists, are also committed to NATO, although not all would be directly available for use in the European theatre. With the Far East and the entire Pacific to defend, the strategy and location of the war would determine how many troops could be diverted to Europe. Moreover, with more than 300 Soviet submarines hunting specifically for troopships, it is doubtful whether significant reinforcements would get through.

Feeling threatened by the large numbers of Warsaw Pact troops, politicians in Western Europe, supported by others in the USA, favoured the deployment of nuclear weapons. But at the end of the war in 1945, European countries had to choose between reduced defence expenditure and radical social welfare projects to rebuild themselves.

In fact, they chose both options. Europe would have adequate defence and the domestic policies it wanted by uniting under the US nuclear umbrella. In return, the USA was given bases in Europe from which to operate conventional forces and, perhaps, avoid escalation to a major nuclear war if fighting began near the East European border.

Despite this happy arrangement between old allies, Europe has always hoped it would never have to call on the US promise of protection, because the USA might choose not to fight on Europe's behalf for fear of its own devastation. Not surprisingly, Britain began in 1946 to develop its own nuclear force.

The USA was opposed to the spread of nuclear weapons, and saw danger in their acquisition by other countries, just as the superpowers and Britain and France do

today when reports appear about small countries acquiring nuclear weapons. Nevertheless, the USA relented, but stipulated that Germany should never build or control nuclear weapons. (The Luftwaffe does, however, *operate* 72 Pershing 1A missiles under 'dual key' control.)

As plans moved ahead for an independent British nuclear deterrent, European leaders realized that without spending large sums, NATO member states could deploy a large force of small tactical, nuclear weapons. These would present a fearsome line of nuclear retaliation at the slightest East European provocation. Reluctantly, the plan was accepted by the USA, and from the late 1950s, nuclear weapons have formed a leading part of the NATO strategy to stop a Warsaw Pact invasion.

Balancing the budget

As the nuclear theatre forces were building up in Europe, governments were able to reduce significantly their defence

budgets. The US government contributed both the strategic nuclear umbrella and conventional forces, spending between 23 and 50 per cent of its annual budget on defence, whereas European countries reduced theirs to about 10 per cent.

Nevertheless, many European governments thought there should be greater US expenditure on protecting them from Warsaw Pact threats, especially since military might had been used to crush civil disorder in Hungary and Czechoslovakia. Effectively, they wanted a guarantee that the USA would consider the early use of tactical nuclear weapons in a conflict.

The prevailing view in Washington was that an early resort to small nuclear weapons would erode all distinction between conventional war and all-out nuclear war. As a compromise to ease European fears of being overrun by the vast army of Warsaw Pact tanks, it was suggested that in the event of aggression, a series of nuclear demonstrations could be let off in the

Above **France's Mirage IVA forms part of her nuclear deterrence which, although totally independent, is allied to NATO. Britain's contribution to NATO includes her fleet of nuclear submarines – among them HMS** *Renown* **(***left***). Perhaps the deadliest of the weapons which are to be deployed by the West is the US Cruise missile. There are three versions, designed to be launched from a ship, an aircraft (***far right***) or the ground (***right***).**

ESTIMATED LONG AND MEDIUM RANGE NUCLEAR SYSTEMS FOR THE EUROPEAN THEATRE			
NATO SYSTEM	NUMBER OF SYSTEMS	WARHEADS PER SYSTEM	TOTAL WARHEADS
INTERMEDIATE RANGE BALLISTIC MISSILES			
SSBS S-3	18	1	18
SHORT RANGE BALLISTIC MISSILES			
PERSHING 1A	180	1	180
SUBMARINE LAUNCHED BALLISTIC MISSILES			
POLARIS A-3[1]	64	1	64
MSBS M-20	80	1	80
SUBTOTAL	342		342
LAND-BASED AIRCRAFT			
VULCAN B-2[2]	48	2	96
F-111 E/F[2]	156	2	312
MIRAGE IVA	34	1	34
BUCCANEER[2]	50	2	100
F-104	290	1	290
F-4	424	1	424
F-16	68	1	68
JAGUAR	117	1	117
MIRAGE IIIE	30	1	30
CARRIER-BASED AIRCRAFT			
A-6E	20	2	40
A-7E	48	2	96
SUPER ETENDARD	16	2	32
SUBTOTAL	1301		1639
TOTAL	1643		1981
1 See text			
2 To be replaced by Tornado aircraft			

WARSAW PACT SYSTEM	NUMBER OF SYSTEMS	WARHEADS PER SYSTEM	TOTAL WARHEADS
INTERMEDIATE RANGE BALLISTIC MISSILES			
SS-20	315	3	945
SS-5 SKEAN[1]	16	1	16
MEDIUM RANGE BALLISTIC MISSILES			
SS-4 SANDAL[1]	275	1	275
SHORT RANGE BALLISTIC MISSILES			
SS-12 SCALEBOARD	70	1	70
SCUD A/B	450	1	450
SCUD B/C	143	1	143
SS-22	100	1	100
SS-23	10	1	10
SUBMARINE LAUNCHED BALLISTIC MISSILES			
SS-N-5 SERB	57	1	57
SUBTOTAL	1436		2066
AIRCRAFT			
TU-26 (TU-22M) BACKFIRE B	100	4	400
TU-16 BADGER	310	2	620
TU-22 BLINDER	125	2	250
SU-24 (SU-19) FENCER	550	2	1100
MiG-27 FLOGGER D	550	1	550
SU-17 FITTER C/D	688	1	688
SU-7 FITTER A	265	1	265
MiG-21 FISHBED J-N	100	1	100
SUBTOTAL	2688		3973
TOTAL	4124		6039
1 Being phased out			

Mediterranean, perhaps, to warn the Soviets of NATO's seriousness. The Soviet response to the idea of such a warning shot shocked Western opinion in the early 1980s, when it was realized that NATO's plan to defuse a conflict in this way would actually have the opposite effect.

Differences in US and European views on nuclear strategy worsened when West German Chancellor Helmut Schmidt's direct appeals for stronger nuclear weapons in Europe were ignored by President Ford. Eventually, concerted efforts by the German Chancellor and Britain's Prime Minister, James Callaghan, were successful when the seriousness of European fears of Soviet triple-warhead SS-20 mobile missiles were made known.

President Carter agreed to replace 108 Pershing 1A missiles with 108 of the much longer range Pershing 2, and to deploy 464 sea-launched Cruise missiles on land laun-

Aircraft feature strongly in any plan to fight a tactical nuclear war. And as the weapons ranged across the battle line become more sophisticated, ways must be found to minimize the cost. One method is to combine the roles of fighter and bomber – this is the principle of the multi-role combat aircraft. The General Dynamics F-16 (*right*) is an impressive example. It is a lightweight, agile, difficult-to-engage fighter as well as an able nuclear bomber. The engine is similar to that used in the twin-engined F-15 Eagle, but it is the aircraft's advanced aerodynamics and control systems that make it among the most successful of its type. The Panavia Tornado (*below*) is a replacement for several older types, including Buccaneers, Starfighters, Vulcans and Canberras. The replacement will be completed by 1990.

chers in Britain, West Germany, Italy, Belgium and the Netherlands. In addition, the Pershing 1A missiles operated by West Germany will be replaced by Pershing 2s.

The commitment was made in 1979 with the expressed hope that disarmament talks would remove the need for any missiles of this type to be deployed. Three years later, little or no progress had been made. Seeking to revitalize the defence debate, politicians across Europe offered alternative strategies and proposed new initiatives, from all-out European nuclear disarmament to a reinvigorated central European independent nuclear defence strategy.

Trident 2

Britain has decided to replace 64 Polaris missiles and four submarines with a Trident 2 force that, if numerically the same as the Polaris fleet, will provide 640 warheads against 640 targets, compared with the present list of 64 separate targets addressed by Polaris. (Each Polaris carries three 200 kiloton warheads, but since these are not independently targetable they are usually counted as a single warhead. The Chevaline variant of the Polaris, which will be carried by four of the UK's missile submarines until Trident is introduced, has six

50 kiloton warheads.)

By the end of the decade, Britain and Italy will have 530 Tornado aircraft capable of delivering 1060 nuclear warheads, even if only one mission per aircraft is counted. In addition, there are 250 F-16 fighter-bombers in the Netherlands, each capable of carrying a single nuclear weapon, 48 Mirage 2000 aircraft in France and 100 F-104 Starfighters in several European countries.

France is not part of NATO, but it is committed to train with NATO forces for the probable role it would have in a European war. By 1990, France will have 112 single warhead missiles on seven submarines, 18 in land-based silos and a new mobile missile to replace the Mirage IVA nuclear bomber in service since the early 1960s.

Collectively, without US contributions of any kind, the West European inventory would amount to more than 2200 nuclear warheads on about 1100 delivery systems. Surprisingly, this is more than a third of the number of Soviet warheads facing European NATO forces today. But amidst calls for all nuclear weapons to be removed from Europe, the governments are continuing to strengthen their nuclear arsenals.

The General Dynamics FB-111 is the bomber mode of a multi-role aircraft. Instead of bombs, it can carry six short range attack missiles (SRAMs), two within the fuselage and four on pods.

THE BEAM MACHINE

Military strategists believe that the nation that controls space controls the world, and new engines of war will soon make this possible

For many years, scientists have known that light and atomic particles could, separately, provide weapons of unimagined capacity to knock out tanks, aircraft and ships. In the search for new and exciting forms of energy, physicists have shown how near these 'beam' weapons are to reality.

Many years of research to harness the atom's power for peace and war have resulted in a vast amount of knowledge about the probable design of a laser gun or particle-beam device, and by the early 1980s, many military scientists were committed to the idea that lasers and particle beam weapons are the only really effective means of combating a nuclear attack.

The basis of a weapon that could prove highly effective against satellites and missiles is microwave radiation – frequently suggested as a means of transmitting energy from orbiting solar power stations to receptors on the ground. Such a weapon

Below **Recognizing the importance placed by the military on satellites for communication and control, the super-powers have sought a means to rapidly knock out these 'eyes' and 'ears' of a potential enemy. The Soviet anti-satellite weapon can destroy a target at 2 km, but the next stage in space warfare will be laser weapons,** *right.*

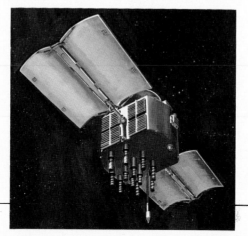

would not be intended to burn or blow up targets, because a microwave beam diverges, or spreads out, rapidly and loses power. Instead, beam powers of up to 100 watts per square centimetre would be used to overload electronic equipment, such as sensors and control circuits, and to jam radar communications.

In the form of *masers*, microwaves can be made powerful, but this technology has largely been superseded by lasers. The word maser is an acronym of Microwave Amplification by Stimulated Emission of Radiation, and masers are the microwave equivalent of lasers, which work by light amplification. The tendency of microwaves to diverge is due to the relatively long wave length. So, the technique of amplifying electromagnetic beams has progressed through the spectrum from masers to infra-red lasers and now ultra-violet lasers, both of progressively shorter wave length.

The potential lethality of lasers comes from the fact that electromagnetic radiation can be amplified and discharged in short, focused pulses, each pulse having a power of many millions of watts. Perfecting a weapons system of this sort is a formidable task, but even more challenging is the problem of aiming the beam. In the battlefield of Earth orbit, for example, the laser light is discharged virtually instantaneously, so there is no scope for mid-course corrections as there is with missiles. Distant targets would need to be selected either electronically or by the aid of high-magnification telescopes, which require extreme stability.

Heat dissipation

When all these technical problems have been solved, there remains the nuisance that such advanced technology can be foiled by measures such as reflectors and ceramic heat dissipators similar to the tiles that shield the Shuttle from the heat generated during re-entry into the atmosphere.

The next stage in laser sophistication is likely to provide a beam that is not only much more powerful, but also highly penetrating, less prone to divergence and immune to countermeasures. This is the *X-raser* – the X-ray equivalent of the laser.

The breakthrough in X-ray lasers came from research into nuclear fusion. Using a technique called *inertial confinement*, scientists discovered that certain materials can be made to emit beams of coherent, amplified X-rays. The technique is to bombard a sample of carbon simultaneously from several directions, using multiple-beam lasers. The sample becomes heated to the point where all but one of the outer electrons are stripped from the atoms, producing carbon-6.

Soft X-rays

For laser action, carbon-6 is excited – pumped with energy so that the sample contains more electrons at high energy levels than at the ground, or normal, state. This condition is called *population inversion*. The excited electrons then return to the ground state, emitting photons as they do, but they descend in stages. At one stage, carbon-6 emits a photon of soft X-ray, just as an excited ruby atom emits a photon of red laser light. X-ray lasers are less efficient than visible light lasers – they require pumping to extremely high energy levels – but they could generate pulses capable of vaporizing targets at 2000 km.

The most effective anti-satellite (Asat) weapon would be one able to fire effectively at all satellites wherever they are located. In that regard, the laser weapon is most efficient. In space, where there is no atmosphere, laser light can be directed with pin-point accuracy to a target. In the atmosphere, however, the effective range of the weapon is restricted severely. So, a laser-Asat in space can make the best use of

Right **Already, space has become the fourth medium (after land, sea and air) for military activity. When laser and other beam weapons have been perfected, they could be made to knock out rockets ascending from silos or submarines, so warheads would not fall on cities and the attack would be stopped as it began.**

the available technology and operate at maximum effect.

Both the USSR and the USA have been researching laser weapons for many years. Long before public announcement of the intention to proceed with these weapons, both sides had made preparations for a major new role for the military in space.

Development times are hard to predict for technology that still needs refinement. It is generally agreed by defence scientists that the first laser-Asat weapons could be in orbit by the end of the 1980s and that a laser-anti-missile system might be possible a decade after that. It is certain, however, that both the USA and the USSR are fully committed to preparing space as a new theatre for war. That is already coaxing engineers and design groups to look to the next generation of fighters that might be needed to operate on the fringe of space, attacking enemy satellites or defending space-based activity.

Armed with a range of communication and control satellites and laser gun-ships in space, the USA hopes to be able to defend itself against even the fiercest surprise nuclear attack. An early warning satellite (1) detecting an enemy missile (2) alerts headquarters (4) via a satellite link (3). Authorization (5) results in a kill (6).

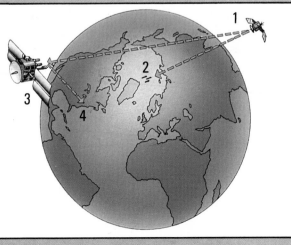

tion to the other side. The USA exercises a ban on a long list of 'sensitive' equipment which may not be exported to the USSR or its satellite states, even though the items may be generally available in the West. Some of the most sensational security scandals of recent years have revolved around the illicit export to the Eastern Bloc of Western high-tech goods. Where strategic items are concerned the ban is understandable. There is no doubt that the Soviet Union lags far behind the West in the field of microcircuitry, and is very eager to obtain advanced microchips for use in programmable weaponry.

The hidden dangers

There are certain obvious dangers inherent in the militarization of science, but others may not be so immediately obvious. All the world is aware of the military development of nuclear weapons, but it is not as widely realized that this growing area of military science could be in danger of monopolizing the scarce resources of scientists and research facilities. When the major available funds come from the defence departments of governments, the pure research of scientists and technicians has to give way to weapons development. Companies with lucrative defence contracts are tempted to move further and further towards the development of military items, particularly when traditional markets are depressed. The international

character of science which enables the poorest as well as the richest nations to benefit from new developments in medicine, food technology and energy conservation, is in great danger of breaking down.

Protectiveness hides it behind locked doors. It will be little consolation that every few years we will gain the equivalent of a non-stick frying-pan as a by-product of a machine gun.

The technology which made possible the development of supersonic passenger flight (*above*) was gleaned from faster than sound spy planes designed to fly reconnaissance missions (*below*). Also radar (*bottom left*), the radio system which allows civilian air traffic to function safely in the ever more congested skies, was designed to give early warning of approaching enemy aircraft.

INDEX

THE KNOCKOUT BLOW

Silent and destructive, the new shock from space

In the aftermath of a nuclear explosion survivors will not only have to cope with the terrible consequences of the fireball and radioactive fall out, but also with a complete breakdown of all communications systems. For, as well as the expected physical effects of the bomb there is also another invisible and potentially more damaging phenomenon – the electromagnetic pulse. Its effect is tantamount to wiring every electrical circuit in the area to a very high voltage for a very short time. The circuits simply overload and burn out.

In a high level nuclear explosion (40 km-500 km above ground zero) gamma rays are generated. These high energy rays travel away from the point of the explosion at the speed of light, 300 million metres per second. They are of extremely high intensity and are generated within nanoseconds (10^{-9}s) of the blast.

As they travel through the upper atmosphere, the gamma rays collide with air molecules. These collisions result in what are called Compton recoil electrons, which are negatively charged, being emitted. The air becomes heavily ionized and the accelerating Compton electrons are deflected by the Earth's magnetic field in such a way that an electric current actually flows in the upper atmosphere, in a direction parallel to the surface of the Earth.

A high level nuclear explosion, 500 km above America, could knock out all communications systems in the country (*above*). High energy gamma rays are emitted from the blast causing massive ionization of the air. This leads to an EMP being set up.

The flow of current is analogous to the currents in a radio transmitting antenna. Because of the extremely fast rise times of the EMP the range of frequencies covered by this atmospheric antenna are very wide. The electric field strength set up in the air can be as high as 50 kV/m. This intense pulse of electromagnetic radiation at virtually all frequencies simultaneously also covers an enormous ground area. A single nuclear blast at an altitude of 500 km could blanket a country the size of the United States.

Just as any conducting object has currents induced in it by the electric and magnetic fields generated by radio transmitting antennae so any metallic conductor within the EMP area would act as a receiving antenna and current would flow in it. Because the range of frequencies generated by EMP is so large all electrical power systems which operate between 50 or 60 Hz as well as all electronic systems operating from dc through to hundreds of gigahertz will be affected.

In power lines which cross the country peak voltages as high as 3MV and peak currents up to 10 kA, yielding peak power of 30,000 MW, could be induced. These enormous surges will not only cause immediate country-wide power black-outs but permanently damage the network by destroying the insulation.

As the length and size of electrical connections and components is decreased so their sensitivity to low frequency fields decreases. The EMP however with its intense 'broadband' fields will generate damaging voltages and currents in even the smallest unshielded electronic component. Radios, computers, navigation systems, alarms and radars as well as domestic equipment and even car parts will be damaged or destroyed by EMP.

For military forces EMP poses a special problem because warning systems that verify a threat and alert counter actions would be destroyed at once. The satellite communications systems that have been developed as a secure radio link are particularly vulnerable to EMP as of course are their ground receivers.

The costly shield

Protection from EMP is complex and costly. It is possible to shield sensitive conductors. And, though power lines cannot be buried, the communications cells and computers can.

Aircraft, satellites, naval vessels and vehicles have metallic skins, which help protect them from the effects of the pulse, but like a ship's hull these have to be 100 per cent intact to prevent the incursion of electromagnetic energy.

When systems are so light that they can not be given a skin, for example a portable radio or missile guidance unit, then the components must be designed to increase protection. The more complex a system the more vulnerable it is to EMP. It would take about 10,000 times more EMP energy to damage a thermionic valve found in older radio equipment than it would to damage a modern silicon integrated circuit.

The Soviet Union used this knowledge in the design of their MiG-23, which, when a pilot defected to Japan in 1978, was discovered to have only thermionic devices in the systems mounted near the fuselage skin, while semi-conductor circuits were housed deep within the aircraft.

Defence systems

In modern systems even the interconnection between components on a printed circuit board can act as receiving antennae. Their geometry and orientation to one another is so important that any connection with the outside world is a threat to the whole system.

Moreover, the use of carbon-fibre reinforced plastics in aircraft has reduced the shielding for electronic equipment that used to be afforded by aluminium.

Research into EMP has led to the development of SGEMP, formerly IEMP – System Generated Electromagnetic Pulse as opposed to Internal Electromagnetic Pulse. In this approach SGEMP is used to see how well shielded systems are – particularly satellites.

A simpler system is that of Current Injection Tests (CIT) which though they do not replace radiation tests offer a relatively inexpensive and easily implemented technique to evaluate some aspects of spacecraft hardness (ability to withstand EMP).

The tremendous progress in the field of fibre optics has provided one very effective way of avoiding EMP damage, for the signals are pulses of light along 'light pipes' (fibre optic bundles). These fibre optic cables are immune to electromagnetic interference and so are ideally suited to EMP vulnerable systems. The threat of EMP damage may be leading to a new era in communications technology. Light and its amazing properties may be the way ahead.

The effects of the EMP on military equipment is of paramount importance. Simulators are used (*right*) to see how effective aircraft are at withstanding EMP bombardment. The B-52 bomber is tested at a base in New Mexico.

The gamma rays strike air molecules in the atmosphere, knocking out high-energy Compton recoil electrons in such large numbers an electric current is set up (*above*). The current is picked up by electrical equipment causing it to fuse instantly (*above*).

A DEADLY WARNING FOR PLANET EARTH

A global nuclear war would put the survival of mankind in serious doubt

The first nuclear bombs to be used in war were exploded in the skies over the Japanese towns of Hiroshima and Nagasaki on August 6th and 9th, 1945. The effects were devastating. Hundreds of thousands of people were killed instantly. Many more were maimed or injured, and many of the survivors suffered either physically or mentally for the rest of their lives.

Yet today the current world arsenal stands at over 40,000 nuclear warheads, with explosive powers ranging from about one twentieth to over a thousand times the destructive power of the bomb which levelled Hiroshima.

Overkill

The total strength of this arsenal is equivalent to about one million times the power of the Hiroshima bomb, or some thirteen thousand million tonnes of TNT. In frighteningly simple terms there are over three tonnes of high explosive for every man, woman and child on Earth.

The madness of the arms race means that both the USA and the USSR could wipe out each other some twenty to forty times over

Above **A wristwatch from the wreckage of Hiroshima stopped at 8.15 – the moment the bomb detonated.** *Left* **A postwar US atomic bomb test at Bikini Atoll, 1946.**

– this is known as the *overkill* factor – but what would be the consequences for the rest of the world?

Considering the destructive effects of just the two, relatively small, bombs in Japan the consequences of a nuclear war, where even a small fraction of the world arsenal were exploded, is likely to be very severe. But, most authorities agree, if a nuclear war breaks out – however started – by accident, escalation of a border incident, or even a deliberate surprise attack, it is likely to develop into an all-out nuclear war. The accuracy of today's weapons is a crucial factor, encouraging a *first strike* because of the risk of missiles being destroyed by enemy missiles before they can be launched. For these reasons, it is highly likely that most weapons would be used, although many might not work properly. Assuming that roughly a quarter of the weapons did not explode for various reasons, this means that about 10,000 megatons (one megaton is the explosive equivalent of one million tons of TNT) would be used.

The USA, USSR and Europe (particularly

the UK and West Germany, where many American weapons are based) would be the main targets. They would receive about 6000 megatons exploded on the ground, aimed at specific military targets such as missile silo fields, command and communication centres and marshalling yards. An additional 1000-2000 megatons would probably be exploded in the air to achieve the maximum destruction of cities (the blast from a bomb exploded in the air extends further than one exploded on the ground). The remaining 2000-3000 megatons would be aimed at specific military and economic targets on the remaining continents. Countries such as India and China who possess their own nuclear weapons would be targets in their own right. So to a lesser extent would be countries who are either thought to possess their own nuclear weapons or have the ability to construct them, or those who would be considered an economic threat to recovery of either superpower after the war. In this category would come countries such as Israel, South Africa, Pakistan and Japan.

The immediate effects of an all-out nuclear war would be devastating. The First World countries – which are largely situated in the world's northern hemisphere – would suffer most from a nuclear war with 86 per cent of their populations dead or injured. This is because most of their populations are concentrated in urban areas and so extremely vulnerable to nuclear attack. In the less heavily targeted and more rural Third World countries about 46 per cent of the population would be dead or injured.

The toll

Considering the world as a whole about 1600 million people would be killed and 930 million injured by the initial effects of heat, blast and radiation. Blast related injuries would account for 58 per cent of fatal

Above **The memory of a five-year-old boy of the detonation of the bomb at Hiroshima.** *Left* **Survivors of the blast seek refuge less than an hour after the explosion.** *Right* **Mother and child a day after, having received emergency rations.** *Far right top* **700 metres south of the hypocentre at Nagasaki.** *Far right* **Mother and child being returned to Nagasaki some days after the bombing.** *Below* **Hiroshima.**

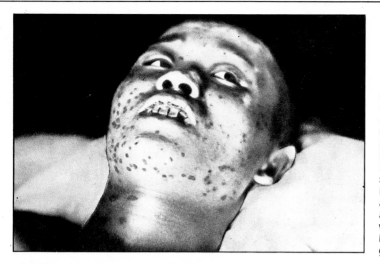

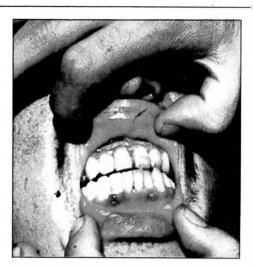

Left **A 21-year-old soldier two hours before he died of radiation sickness. Purple spots of hypodermal bleeding cover his face and upper body. He was guarding a building one kilometre north-east of the hypocentre in Hiroshima. The sickness showed itself two weeks after the explosion and he died two weeks later.** *Right* **Bleeding of the gums was common.**

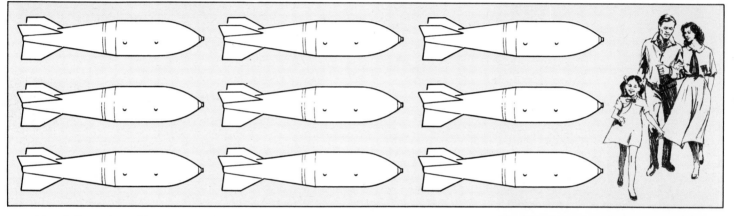

Above **The arms race hinges on MAD (mutually assured destruction). The result is three tonnes of high explosive for every person on Earth.** *Right* **Bertrand Russell saying 'No' to nuclear madness.**

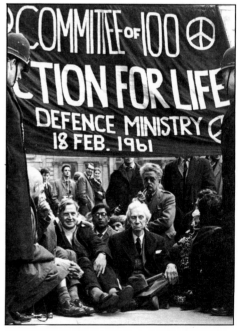

casualties followed by 33 per cent from acute radiation doses and 9 per cent from burns and fire.

In towns and cities large numbers of animal and human corpses combined with the breakdown of water and sewage services would mean infectious diseases, always latent in the population, such as cholera, typhus, tuberculosis and dysentery would spread rapidly. Any medical services remaining would be completely overwhelmed by sheer numbers of injured and sick and the lack of drugs, doctors, power supplies or uncontaminated water. Radiation poisoning would also be an ever-present danger. Fires would rage until they burnt themselves out.

The long term

In the longer term there would be economic chaos. Industrial and agricultural production would virtually halt in the USA, USSR, Eastern Europe, Western Europe, the Middle East and Japan. Over 90 per cent of the manufacturing capacity of South Africa, India, China and Indonesia would have been destroyed. Widespread starvation would occur in much of the Third World as the total collapse of the international network of trade and exchange took effect. This could lead to one and a half billion additional deaths due to starvation and disease as Third World populations were brutally reduced to their natural pre-industrial levels.

As a result of these factors casualty fi-

gures six months after World War III could be over 1000 million dead in the First World and 2300 million dead in the Third World countries, bringing the total to 3300 million – over *three-quarters* of the world's population.

These figures, bad as they are, take no account of the global pollution of water supplies by radioactive elements or damage to the Earth's atmosphere and ecosystem which could combine irreversibly to unbalance the environment. The effects of radiation would favour the rapid increase in insects and other pests as their natural predators succumbed more readily to radiation. The crops that remained would suffer accordingly, and the food value of future harvests would be jeopardized by harmful mutations brought about by radiation. In any case, many croplands and forest areas would be devastated in huge fires which would burn for weeks – corresponding to a flaming land area the combined size of Denmark, Norway and Sweden. In the northern hemisphere, these fires, together with conflagrations started in oil fields and refineries, would produce a thick smoke layer that would drastically reduce the amount of sunlight reaching the Earth's surface. Some research suggests that this *darkness*

at noon would persist for many weeks.

Life on the Earth as a whole relies on the existence of a thin layer of ozone high in the atmosphere which filters out the harmful ultra-violet rays of the Sun. The explosion of several thousand nuclear weapons would inject massive amounts of nitrogen oxides into the atmosphere. The mechanisms of ozone creation and destruction are not fully understood, but a significant reduction in the ozone layer is likely. If this were to hap-

pen life on Earth would become quite intolerable. A 50 per cent reduction in the ozone layer would result in gradual blindness to all animals and insects. The ecosystem would be disastrously disrupted and, without the chance of evolutionary adjustments, many plant and animal species would become extinct. With such catastrophic effects upon the environment the survival of mankind would seriously be in doubt.

At best we can expect a recovery time to our present standards of at least decades and possibly centuries. Most of the world's remaining population would be in the southern hemisphere, mainly in sub-Saharan Africa and Latin America. These survivors of famine, disease and radiation would exist in war economies geared to pure survival in a social and economic dark age, based largely on primitive agriculture.

At worst there would be no survivors. The ozone layer would be depleted. Climatic changes due to soot deposition and high levels of carbon dioxide from fires would lead to the melting of the polar icecaps. The Earth would be almost devoid of life.

Nobody can tell what the fate of mankind would be, but either conclusion comes as a stark warning to the superpowers who can in no way win a large-scale nuclear war. Each side would be a loser as our civilization was destroyed in a holocaust of a few hours' or days' duration.

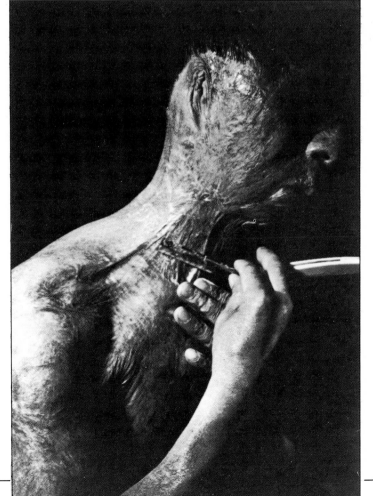

Above **Life on Earth depends on a fragile balance of nature. Depicted here are typical food chains on land and in the sea and the circulation of life-nourishing waters. A global nuclear war would disrupt the chains significantly. The reduction of the protective ozone layer could allow harmful quantities of ultra-violet rays to blind many animals and insects. Many plants and animals would suffer extinction, the food chains would be broken, and pests, bacteria and disease would proliferate. Life for the surviving populations of the world would at best be extremely primitive, and at worst, impossible.** *Left* **Yamaguchi Senji was 14 when the second nuclear bomb fell, on his native Nagasaki. This picture, 1970.**

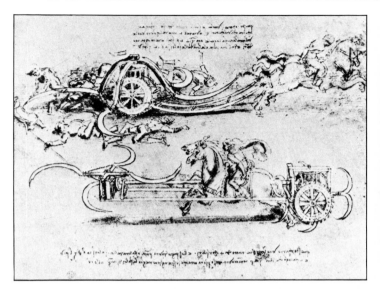

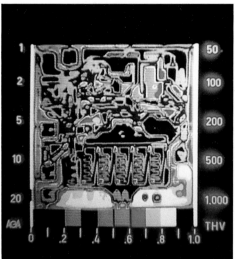

Far left **Leonardo da Vinci's skills were employed by the Italian government to produce machines of war.** *Left* **Today, micro-chip technology is fuelled by military needs.** *Below* **Teflon was an underused discovery before defence scientists applied its non-stick properties to increasing the efficiency of machine guns. Now it coats not only frying pans but also the sewing rings in artificial heart valves** (*insert*).

WAR AND PEACE

Necessity is the mother of invention and nothing, for most nations, is more necessary than defence

The most pressing priority of nation states throughout history has been military survival and victory. Necessity is the mother of invention, so it is hardly surprising that the leading edge of scientific discovery and development has so often been military in nature. Both Archimedes, in Ancient Greece, and Leonardo da Vinci, in Renaissance Italy, were employed as military engineers, so that their military wages can be seen, in some ways, as having subsidized the great works for which they are justly more famous in the modern world.

The research that produces and refines today's weapon systems is carried out not in the workshops and studios of individual scientists and artists, but in the laboratories of universities, multinational companies and defence departments of governments. Since weapons development became big business, both governments and private companies have channelled seemingly bottomless funds into research and development (R and D). In many industrialized countries the Defence Ministry or its equivalent is as much an organ of competitive

HUD OPTICAL SYSTEM

Aircraft
windscreen

Combining
glass

Cathode ray tube
image on
combining glass

Pilot's line of sight

Collimating
lens for
infinity
image

Cathode
ray tube

Mirror

industry as of national defence concerns.

Military scientific researchers and discoveries have always had civilian implications. The artifacts of the Iron Age were weapons before they were tools. Boat development through the centuries has always been led by military designs. When the Great War broke out in 1914 only eleven years had elapsed since the Wright Brothers had made the world's first powered flight, yet already the Germans were mass producing military aircraft. The heavy demands of war, and the need for manoeuvrable, tough machines, dragged the aeroplane out of the era of string and glue and into the modern armour-plated world, where military designs are still the forerunners of most civil aircraft.

The arms race

The incentives and government encouragement towards bigger and better weapons systems have increased several-fold since the confrontation politics of the great powers have become measured in terms of arms races. The material rewards are enormous for those gaining the major contracts. In 1981 a rough estimate of the world's total expenditure on defence-related equipment was around $650 billion, and for the third year in a row, despite a deteriorating world economy, the annual expenditure figure was up some three per cent on the previous year's figures.

In the West a hefty proportion of this massive expenditure goes to private industry. A good example of a growth area in military spending on new technology is that of anti-submarine warfare (ASW). In 1982 the US government spent $11.3 billion on this technology alone, with a 6.5 per cent increase scheduled for the following fiscal year. In 1982 the biggest rise in the ASW budget was for research funds, which totalled over 20 per cent of the US Navy's total $5.8 billion R and D budget.

The Edo Corporation, Gould, Hughes, Bendix and Western Electric are all major

Above **The special demands of combat flying led to the development of the head-up display (HUD) system. The optical system** (*above right*) **projects the computer generated data into the pilot's line of sight, adjusting the light rays in such a way that the display characters appear to be focused at infinity, so avoiding the need to re-focus the eyes when reading them. The car of tomorrow** (*right*) **may well make use of HUD technology to replace conventional instrumentation.**

suppliers of Tactical Towed Array Sonar, a recent innovation consisting of long strings of cable-mounted hydrophones capable of picking up enemy submarine traces at long range. Hull-mounted passive sonar systems are made by IBM and Raytheon, while free-floating sonobuoys are also being developed for the Department of Defense by private contractors. Sonar developments can have a spin-off effect for civilian industries with improved navigation and deep-sea fishing techniques. Less useful to the civilian sector is the development of advanced lightweight torpedoes for ASW work, for which a large chunk of the development budget is also earmarked.

For pinpointing submarines that have been indicated by such detectors as sonobuoys and other acoustic sensors, the US Navy employs a device known as MAD, which stands for Magnetic Anomaly Detector. MAD is a magnetometer carried in an aircraft. Magnetometers are used to measure the Earth's magnetic field, and metal submarines show up on MAD's screens as

'anomalies'. Civilian usage of this system could include the prospecting for metal ore deposits beneath the oceans. The processing of complex sonar messages is one of the many areas where military science employs increasing amounts of computer technology. Already the Defense establishment in the USA is the major purchaser of advanced microcomputer chips, and all the purest and best quality silicon based microcircuits are reserved for military use.

Non-stick bullets

The non-stick frying pan was made possible by military research in a roundabout way. Although the Du Pont company had accidentally come across polytetrafluoroethylene (PTFE) in the research labs, they had no use for it until the US Naval Research Laboratory discovered a method of applying it to surfaces. The Navy was interested in reducing friction in machine-gun bullet chambers, but the civilian uses of Teflon as it is now called range from kitchen-ware to bionic surgery.

The link between space research and military R and D has always been close, and as both major superpowers seek to extend their arenas of power, space research has become almost synonymous with military research. It is no accident that most astronauts of both sides are drawn from military personnel.

In the USA there has been an overt shift from the NASA researches of the Jet Propulsion Laboratory, which leads Western space exploration, to a more direct link with the US Defense Department. As 'straight' space research projects such as the Venus mapping mission become priced out of feasibility in times of tight budgets, the JPL has shifted to the more readily available

funds of the Defense Department, and work on defence satellites. One project is to make orbiting satellites less dependent on input from the ground. Using computerized programmes of a sort developed for deep space probes, the military satellites will monitor their own systems, detect problems as they occur, and correct them, as well as carrying out automatic routine maintenance.

In the science fiction world of direct energy weapons ('death rays'), much work is being carried out by both sides in the arms race. This is a region which can have few peaceful spin-offs for the non-military world. Lasers are central to this research. The Soviet Union appears to be far ahead of

the West in this technology, and is carrying out programmes up to five times the size of those under way in the USA. Some observers believe that the Soviets could be deploying laser weapons by the mid 1980s. In the Soviet Union the division between military and civilian science is even less clear than it is in the West. Over half of the USSR's 900,000 R and D scientists and engineers are busy on military projects, according to the Pentagon.

In the decade up to 1980 the Soviet Union flew 17 anti-satellite (Asat) tests, and this uniquely military aspect of space research is common to both the USSR and the USA. The Russian tests involve the use of 'killer-satellites' while the US research is focusing on fighter-launched missiles and ground-based lasers. The Soviet killer-satellites operate by being launched into an orbit below that of their target, gaining altitude to intercept swiftly, within one orbit of the Earth, and exploding next to the target.

Spy satellites

For unmanned reconnaissance the Soviets are developing a solar-powered satellite that can stay in orbit for a month at a time, filming without a break, periodically ejecting re-entry modules containing exposed film. The US is dispensing with the need for film altogether by using spy satellites that transmit digital images.

A major casualty of the military competition between the scientific communities of East and West is the free exchange of information. Information broadcast from space research equipment is usually in code so that only the launcher can benefit from the transmissions. Secrecy extends to all areas of research and development as the paranoid superpowers try to deny informa-